AS-Level
Chemistry

The Revision Guide
Exam Board: OCR A

Editors:

Mary Falkner, Sarah Hilton, Paul Jordin, Sharon Keeley, Simon Little, Andy Park.

Contributors:

Antonio Angelosanto, Vikki Cunningham, Ian H. Davis, John Duffy, Max Fishel, Emma Grimwood, Richard Harwood, Lucy Muncaster, Glenn Rogers, Derek Swain, Paul Warren, Chris Workman.

Proofreaders:

Barrie Crowther, Julie Wakeling.

Published by Coordination Group Publications Ltd.

ISBN: 978 1 84762 126 9

With thanks to Jan Greenway for the copyright research.

With thanks to Science Photo Library for permission to reproduce the photographs used on pages 93 and 94.

Graph to show trend in atmospheric CO_2 Concentration and global temperature on page 92 based on data by EPICA Community Members 2004 and Siegenthaler et al 2005.

Groovy website: www.cgpbooks.co.uk
Jolly bits of clipart from CorelDRAW®
Printed by Elanders Hindson Ltd, Newcastle upon Tyne.

Contents

The Scientific Process

'How Science Works' is all about the scientific process — how we develop and test scientific ideas.
It's what scientists do all day, every day (well except at coffee time — never come between scientists and their coffee).

Scientists Come Up with **Theories** — Then **Test Them**...

Science tries to explain **how** and **why** things happen. It's all about seeking and gaining **knowledge** about the world around us. Scientists do this by **asking** questions and **suggesting** answers and then **testing** them, to see if they're correct — this is the **scientific process**.

1) **Ask** a question — make an **observation** and ask **why or how** whatever you've observed happens.
E.g. Why does sodium chloride dissolve in water?

2) **Suggest** an answer, or part of an answer, by forming a **theory** or a **model** (a possible **explanation** of the observations or a description of what you think is happening actually happening).
E.g. Sodium chloride is made up of charged particles which are pulled apart by the polar water molecules.

3) Make a **prediction** or **hypothesis** — a **specific testable statement**, based on the theory, about what will happen in a test situation.
E.g. A solution of sodium chloride will conduct electricity much better than water does.

4) Carry out **tests** — to provide **evidence** that will support the prediction or refute it.
E.g. Measure the conductivity of water and of sodium chloride solution.

The evidence supported Quentin's Theory of Flammable Burps.

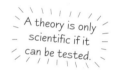

A theory is only scientific if it can be tested.

...Then They **Tell** Everyone About Their **Results**...

The results are **published** — scientists need to let others know about their work. Scientists publish their results in **scientific journals**. These are just like normal magazines, only they contain **scientific reports** (called papers) instead of the latest celebrity gossip.

1) Scientific reports are similar to the **lab write-ups** you do in school. And just as a lab write-up is **reviewed** (marked) by your teacher, reports in scientific journals undergo **peer review** before they're published.

   Scientists use standard terminology when writing their reports. This way they know that other scientists will understand them. For instance, there are internationally agreed rules for naming organic compounds, so that scientists across the world will know exactly what substance is being referred to. See page 49.

2) The report is sent out to **peers** — other scientists who are experts in the **same area**. They go through it bit by bit, examining the methods and data, and checking it's all clear and logical. When the report is approved, it's **published**. This makes sure that work published in scientific journals is of a **good standard**.

3) But peer review **can't guarantee** the science is **correct** — other scientists still need to **reproduce** it.

4) Sometimes **mistakes** are made and bad work is published. Peer review **isn't perfect** but it's probably the best way for scientists to self-regulate their work and to publish **quality reports**.

...Then **Other Scientists** Will **Test** the Theory Too

1) Other scientists read the published theories and results, and try to **test the theory** themselves. This involves:
   - Repeating the **exact same experiments**.
   - Using the theory to make **new predictions** and then testing them with **new experiments**.

2) If all the experiments in the world provide evidence to back it up, the theory is thought of as **scientific 'fact'** (for now).

3) If **new evidence** comes to light that **conflicts** with the current evidence the theory is questioned all over again. More rounds of **testing** will be carried out to try to find out where the theory **falls down**.

This is how the scientific process works — evidence supports a theory, loads of other scientists read it and test it for themselves, eventually all the scientists in the world agree with it and then bingo, you get to learn it.

This is exactly how scientists arrived at the structure of the atom (see pages 6-7) — and how they came to the conclusion that electrons are arranged in shells and orbitals (see page 22). It took years and years for these models to be developed and accepted — this is often the case with the scientific process.

The Scientific Process

If the **Evidence** Supports a Theory, It's **Accepted** — **for Now**

Our currently accepted theories have survived this '**trial by evidence**'. They've been tested **over and over again** and each time the results have backed them up. **BUT**, and this is a big but (teehee), they never become totally indisputable fact. Scientific **breakthroughs or advances** could provide new ways to question and test the theory, which could lead to **changes and challenges** to it. Then the testing starts all over again...

And this, my friend, is the **tentative nature of scientific knowledge** — it's always **changing** and **evolving**.

When CFCs were first used in fridges in the 1930s, scientists thought they were problem-free — well, why not? There was no evidence to say otherwise. It was decades before anyone found out that CFCs were actually making a whopping great hole in the ozone layer. See page 94.

Evidence Comes From **Lab Experiments**...

1) Results from **controlled experiments** in **laboratories** are **great**.
2) A lab is the easiest place to **control variables** so that they're all **kept constant** (except for the one you're investigating).
3) This means you can draw meaningful **conclusions**.

For example, if you're investigating how temperature affects the rate of a reaction you need to keep everything but the temperature constant, e.g. the pH of the solution, the concentration of the solution, etc.

...But You **Can't** Always do a Lab Experiment

There are things you **can't** study in a lab. And outside the lab controlling the variables is tricky, if not impossible.

*   *Are increasing CO_2 emissions causing climate change?*
    There are other variables which may have an effect, such as changes in solar activity. You can't easily rule out every possibility. Also, climate change is a very **gradual process**. Scientists won't be able to tell if their predictions are correct for donkey's years.

    See pages 92-93 for more on climate change.

*   *Does drinking chlorinated tap water increase the risk of developing certain cancers?*
    There are always differences between groups of people. The best you can do is to have a **well-designed study** using **matched groups** — **choose two groups** of people (those who drink tap water and those who don't) which are **as similar as possible** (same mix of ages, same mix of diets etc). But you still can't rule out every possibility. Taking new-born identical twins and treating them identically, except for making one drink gallons of tap water and the other only pure water, might be a fairer test, but it would present huge **ethical problems**.

Samantha thought her study was very well designed — especially the fitted bookshelf.

Science Helps to Inform **Decision-Making**

Lots of scientific work eventually leads to **important discoveries** that **could** benefit humankind — but there are often **risks** attached (and almost always **financial costs**).

Society (that's you, me and everyone else) must weigh up the information in order to **make decisions** — about the way we live, what we eat, what we drive, and so on. Information is also be used by **politicians** to devise policies and laws.

*   **Chlorine** is added to water in **small quantities** to disinfect it. Some studies link drinking chlorinated water with certain types of cancer (see page 47). But the risks from drinking water contaminated by nasty bacteria are far, far greater. There are other ways to get rid of bacteria in water, but they're heaps **more expensive**.
*   Scientific advances mean that **non-polluting hydrogen-fuelled cars** can be made. They're better for the environment, but are really expensive. Also, it'd cost a fortune to adapt the existing filling stations to store hydrogen.
*   Pharmaceutical drugs are really expensive to develop, and drug companies want to make money. So they put most of their efforts into developing drugs that they can sell for a good price. Society has to consider the **cost** of buying new drugs — the **NHS** can't afford the most expensive drugs without **sacrificing** something else.

So there you have it — how science works...

Hopefully these pages have given you a nice intro to how science works, e.g. what scientists do to provide you with 'facts'. You need to understand this, as you're expected to know how science works yourselves — for the exam and for life.

The Atom

This stuff about atoms and elements should be ingrained in your brain from GCSE. You do need to know it perfectly though if you are to negotiate your way through the field of man-eating tigers which is AS Chemistry.

Atoms are made up of **Protons**, **Neutrons** and **Electrons**

Atoms are the stuff **all** elements and compounds are made of.
They're made up of 3 types of particle — **protons**, **neutrons** and **electrons**.

Electrons
1) Electrons have **-1** charge.
2) They whizz around the nucleus in **orbitals**. The orbitals take up most of the **volume** of the atom.

Nucleus
1) Most of the **mass** of the atom is concentrated in the nucleus.
2) The **diameter** of the nucleus is rather titchy compared to the whole atom.
3) The nucleus is where you find the **protons** and **neutrons**.

The mass and charge of these subatomic particles is **really small**, so **relative mass** and **relative charge** are used instead.

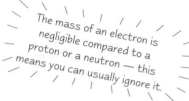
The mass of an electron is negligible compared to a proton or a neutron — this means you can usually ignore it.

Subatomic particle	Relative mass	Relative charge
Proton	1	+1
Neutron	1	0
Electron, e^-	$\frac{1}{2000}$	−1

Nuclear Symbols Show Numbers of **Subatomic Particles**

You can figure out the **number** of protons, neutrons and electrons from the **nuclear symbol**.

Mass (nucleon) number
This tells you the **total** number of **protons** and **neutrons** in the nucleus.

Element symbol

$$_Z^A X$$

Sometimes the atomic number is left out of the nuclear symbol, e.g. ^{7}Li. You don't really need it because the element's symbol tells you its value.

Atomic (proton) number
1) This is the number of **protons** in the nucleus — it identifies the element.
2) **All** atoms of the same element have the **same** number of protons.

1) For **neutral** atoms, which have no overall charge, the number of electrons is **the same as** the number of protons.
2) The number of neutrons is just **mass number minus atomic number**, i.e. 'top minus bottom' in the nuclear symbol.

Nuclear symbol	Atomic number, Z	Mass number, A	Protons	Electrons	Neutrons
$_3^7$ Li	3	7	3	3	7 − 3 = **4**
$_{35}^{80}$ Br	35	80	35	35	80 − 35 = **45**
$_{12}^{24}$ Mg	12	24	12	12	24 − 12 = **12**

"Hello, I'm Newt Ron..."

Ions have **Different** Numbers of **Protons** and **Electrons**

Negative ions have **more electrons** than protons...
E.g.

Br^- The negative charge means that there's 1 more electron than there are protons. Br has 35 protons (see table above), so Br^- must have 36 electrons. The overall charge = + 35 − 36 = −1.

...and **positive** ions have **fewer electrons** than protons. It kind of makes sense if you think about it.
E.g.

Mg^{2+} The 2+ charge means that there's 2 fewer electrons than there are protons. Mg has 12 protons (see table above), so Mg^{2+} must have 10 electrons. The overall charge = +12 − 10 = +2.

The Atom

Isotopes are Atoms of the Same Element with Different Numbers of Neutrons

Make sure you **learn** this definition and totally **understand** what it means —

Isotopes of an element are atoms with the same number of protons but different numbers of neutrons.

Chlorine-35 and chlorine-37 are examples of isotopes.

Different mass numbers mean different numbers of neutrons.

$35 - 17 = 18$ neutrons ← Different mass numbers mean different numbers of neutrons. → $37 - 17 = 20$ neutrons

$$^{35}_{17}\text{Cl}$$

The **atomic numbers** are the same. **Both** isotopes have 17 protons and 17 electrons.

$$^{37}_{17}\text{Cl}$$

1) It's the **number** and **arrangement** of electrons that decides the **chemical properties** of an element. Isotopes have the **same configuration of electrons**, so they've got the **same** chemical properties.

2) Isotopes of an element do have slightly different **physical properties** though, such as different densities, rates of diffusion, etc. This is because **physical properties** tend to depend more on the **mass** of the atom.

Here's another example — naturally occurring **magnesium** consists of 3 isotopes.

^{24}Mg (79%)	^{25}Mg (10%)	^{26}Mg (11%)
12 protons	12 protons	12 protons
12 neutrons	**13** neutrons	**14** neutrons
12 electrons	12 electrons	12 electrons

The periodic table gives the atomic number for each element. The other number isn't the mass number — it's the relative atomic mass (see page 8). They're a bit different, but you can often assume they're equal — it doesn't matter unless you're doing really accurate work.

Practice Questions

Q1 Draw a diagram showing the structure of an atom, labelling each part.

Q2 Define the term 'isotope' and give an example.

Q3 Draw a table showing the relative charge and relative mass of the three subatomic particles found in atoms.

Q4 Using an example, explain the terms 'atomic number' and 'mass number'.

Q5 Where is the mass concentrated in an atom, and what makes up most of the volume of an atom?

Exam Questions

Q1 Hydrogen, deuterium and tritium are all isotopes of each other.
  a) Identify one similarity and one difference between these isotopes. [2 marks]
  b) Deuterium can be written as ^2H. Determine the number of protons, neutrons and electrons in a neutral deuterium atom. [3 marks]
  c) Write a nuclear symbol for tritium, given that it has 2 neutrons. [1 mark]

Q2 This question relates to the atoms or ions A to D: A. $^{32}\text{S}^{2-}$,   B. ^{40}Ar,   C. ^{30}S,   D. ^{42}Ca.

  a) Identify the similarity for each of the following pairs, justifying your answer in each case.
    (i)   A and B. [2 marks]
    (ii)   A and C. [2 marks]
    (iii) B and D. [2 marks]
  b) Which two of the atoms or ions are isotopes of each other? Explain your reasoning. [2 marks]

Got it learned yet? — Isotope so...

This is a nice straightforward page just to ease you in to things. Remember that positive ions have fewer electrons than protons, and negative ions have more electrons than protons. Get that straight in your mind or you'll end up in a right mess. There's nowt too hard about isotopes neither. They're just the same element with different numbers of neutrons.

Atomic Models

Things ain't how they used to be, you know. Take atomic structure, for starters.

The **Accepted Model** of the **Atom** Has **Changed** Throughout History

The model of the atom you're expected to know (the one on page 4) is the currently **accepted model**. It fits all the observations and evidence we have so far, so we **assume it's true** until someone shows that it's **incomplete or wrong**. In the past, completely different models were accepted, because they fitted the evidence available at the time:

1) Some **ancient Greeks** thought that all matter was made from **indivisible particles**. The Greek word <u>atomos</u> means 'uncuttable'.
2) At the start of the 19th century John Dalton described atoms as **solid spheres**, and said that different types of sphere made up the different elements.
3) But as scientists did more experiments, our currently accepted models began to emerge, with modifications or refinements being made to take account of new evidence.

Experimental Evidence Showed that Atoms **Weren't Solid Spheres**

In 1897 J J Thompson did a whole series of experiments and concluded that atoms **weren't** solid and indivisible.

1) His measurements of **charge** and **mass** showed that an atom must contain even smaller, negatively charged particles. He called these particles 'corpuscles' — we call them **electrons**.
2) The 'solid sphere' idea of atomic structure had to be changed. The new model was known as the '**plum pudding model**' — a positively charged sphere with negative electrons embedded in it.

positively charged 'pudding'

delicious pudding

Rutherford Showed that the **Plum Pudding** Model Was **Wrong**

1) In 1909 Ernest Rutherford and his students Hans Geiger and Ernest Marsden conducted the famous **gold foil experiment**. They fired **alpha particles** (which are positively charged) at an extremely thin sheet of gold.
2) From the plum pudding model, they were expecting **most** of the alpha particles to be deflected **very slightly** by the positive 'pudding' that made up most of an atom.
3) In fact, most of the alpha particles passed **straight through** the gold atoms, and a very small number were deflected **backwards** (through more than 90°). This showed that the plum pudding model **couldn't be right**.
4) So Rutherford came up with a model that **could** explain this new evidence — the **nuclear model** of the atom:

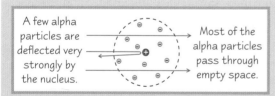
A few alpha particles are deflected very strongly by the nucleus. Most of the alpha particles pass through empty space.

1) There is a **tiny, positively charged nucleus** at the centre of the atom, where most of the atom's mass is concentrated.
2) The nucleus is surrounded by a '**cloud**' of **negative electrons**.
3) Most of the atom is **empty space**.

Rutherford's **Nuclear Model** Was **Modified** Several Times

Rutherford's model seemed pretty convincing, but (there's always a but)... the scientists of the day didn't just say, "Well done Ernest old chap, you've got it", then all move to Patagonia to farm goats. No, they stuck at their experiments, wanting to be sure of the truth. (And it's just conceivable they wanted some fame and fortune too.)

1) Henry Moseley discovered that the charge of the nucleus **increased** from one element to another in units of one.
2) This led Rutherford to investigate the nucleus further. He finally discovered that it contained **positively charged** particles that he called **protons**. The charges of the nuclei of different atoms could then be explained — the atoms of **different elements** have a **different number of protons** in their nucleus.
3) There was still one problem with the model — the nuclei of atoms were **heavier** than they would be if they just contained protons. Rutherford predicted that there were other particles in the nucleus, that had **mass but no charge** — and the **neutron** was eventually discovered by James Chadwick.

> This is nearly always the way scientific knowledge develops — **new evidence** prompts people to come up with **new, improved ideas**. Then other people go through each new, improved idea with a fine-tooth comb as well — modern '**peer review**' (see p2) is part of this process.

Atomic Models

The **Bohr Model** Was a Further Improvement

1) Scientists realised that electrons in a '**cloud**' around the nucleus of an atom would **spiral down** into the nucleus, causing the atom to **collapse**. Niels Bohr proposed a new model of the atom with four basic principles:

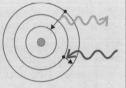

1) Electrons can only exist in **fixed orbits**, or **shells**, and not anywhere in between.
2) Each shell has a **fixed energy**.
3) When an electron moves between shells **electromagnetic radiation** is **emitted** or **absorbed**.
4) Because the energy of shells is fixed, the radiation will have a **fixed frequency**.

2) The frequencies of radiation emitted and absorbed by atoms were already known from experiments. The Bohr model fitted these observations — it looked good.

3) The Bohr model also explained why some elements (the noble gases) are **inert**. He said that the shells of an atom can only hold **fixed numbers of electrons**, and that an element's reactivity is due to its electrons. When an atom has **full shells** of electrons it is **stable** and does not react.

There's **More Than One** Model of Atomic Structure in Use Today

1) We now know that the Bohr model is **not perfect** — but it's still widely used to describe atoms because it's simple and explains many **observations** from experiments, like bonding and ionisation energy trends.

2) The most accurate model we have today involves complicated quantum mechanics. Basically, you can never **know** where an electron is or which direction it's going in at any moment, but you can say **how likely** it is to be at any particular point in the atom. Oh, and electrons can act as **waves** as well as particles (but you don't need to worry about the details).

3) This model might be **more accurate**, but it's a lot harder to get your head round and visualise. It **does** explain some observations that can't be accounted for by the Bohr model though. So scientists use whichever model is most relevant to whatever they're investigating.

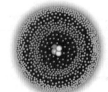

The quantum model of an atom with two shells of electrons. The denser the dots, the more likely an electron is to be there.

Practice Questions

Q1 What particle did J J Thompson discover?

Q2 Describe the model of the atom that was adopted because of Thompson's work.

Q3 Who developed the 'nuclear' model of the atom? What evidence did they have for it?

Q4 What are the names of the two particles in the nucleus of an atom?

Exam Question

Q1 Scientific theories are constantly being revised in the light of new evidence. New theories are accepted if they have been successfully tested by experiments or because they help to explain certain observations.

a) Niels Bohr thought that the model of the atom proposed by Ernest Rutherford did not describe the electrons in an atom correctly. Why did he think this and how was his model of the atom different from Rutherford's? [2 marks]

b) What happens when electrons in an atom move from one shell to another? [1 mark]

c) How did Bohr explain the lack of reactivity of the noble gases? [2 marks]

These models are tiny — even smaller than size zero, I reckon...

The process of developing a model to fit the evidence available, looking for more evidence to show if it's correct or not, then revising the model if necessary is really important. It happens with all new scientific ideas. Remember, scientific 'facts' are only accepted as true because no one's proved yet that they aren't. It might all be bunkum.

Relative Mass

Relative mass... What? Eh?...Read on...

Relative Masses are Masses of Atoms Compared to Carbon-12

The actual mass of an atom is **very**, **very tiny**. Don't worry about exactly how tiny for now, but it's far **too small** to weigh. So, the mass of one atom is compared to the mass of a different atom. This is its **relative mass**. Here are some **definitions** for you to learn:

> The **relative atomic mass**, A_r, is the **average mass** of an atom of an element on a scale where an atom of **carbon-12** is 12.

> Relative atomic mass is an average, so it's not usually a whole number. Relative isotopic mass is always a whole number (at AS level anyway). E.g. a natural sample of chlorine contains a mixture of ^{35}Cl (75%) and ^{37}Cl (25%), so the relative isotopic masses are 35 and 37. But its relative atomic mass is 35.5.

> **Relative isotopic mass** is the mass of an atom of an **isotope** of an element on a scale where an atom of **carbon-12** is 12.

> To find the relative molecular mass, just add up the relative atomic mass values of all the atoms in the molecule,
> e.g. $M_r(C_2H_6O) = (2 \times 12) + (6 \times 1) + 16 = 46$.

> The **relative molecular mass** (or **relative formula mass**), M_r, is the average mass of a **molecule** or **formula unit** on a scale where an atom of **carbon-12** is 12.

> Relative formula mass is used for compounds that are ionic (or giant covalent, such as SiO_2). To find the relative formula mass, add up the relative atomic masses (A_r) of all the ions in the formula unit. (A_r of ion = A_r of atom. The electrons make no difference to the mass.) E.g. $M_r(CaF_2) = 40 + (2 \times 19) = 78$.

A_r Can Be Worked Out from a Isotopic Abundances

You need to know how to calculate the **relative atomic mass** (A_r) of an element from its **isotopic abundances**.

1) Different isotopes of an element occur in different quantities, or **isotopic abundances**. For example, **76%** of the chlorine atoms found on Earth have a relative isotopic mass of 35, while **24%** have a relative isotopic mass of 37.

2) The relative atomic mass of chlorine is the **average** mass of all chlorine atoms. If you've got the isotopic abundances as **percentages**, the easiest way to do this is to imagine you have 100 chlorine atoms, and then find the average mass. Here's the method...

> ***Step 1***: **Multiply** each **relative isotopic mass** by its **% relative isotopic abundance**, and **add up** the results: $(76 \times 35) + (24 \times 37) = 2660 + 888 = \mathbf{3548}$
>
> ***Step 2***: **Divide** by **100**: $3548 \div 100 = \mathbf{35.5}$ (to 1 decimal place)

So the relative atomic mass of chlorine is **35.5** (just like your textbook says).

3) You might be given your isotopic abundances in the form of a **graph**, such as a **mass spectrum**. (Mass spectra are produced by mass spectrometers — devices which are used to find out what samples are made up of by measuring the masses of their components, see page 76.)

For example, using the data from this mass spectrum for neon... ⇨

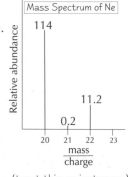

Mass Spectrum of Ne

(treat this as just mass)

> This time the isotopic abundances aren't given as percentages. But just like before...
>
> ***Step 1***: **Multiply** each **relative isotopic mass** by its **relative isotopic abundance**, and **add up** the results: $(20 \times 114) + (21 \times 0.2) + (22 \times 11.2) = \mathbf{2530.6}$
>
> ***Step 2***: **Divide** by the **sum** of the isotopic abundances $(114 + 0.2 + 11.2 = 125.4)$.
> $2530.6 \div 125.4 = \mathbf{20.2}$ (to 1 decimal place)

4) This process of finding an **average** explains why the relative atomic mass is not usually a **whole number**.

Relative Mass

Spreadsheets Can Help You Find Relative Atomic Mass

This method is particularly useful when a large amount of data is being used.
You can put the **relative isotopic abundance** data into a spreadsheet, then get the spreadsheet to work out the A_r for you.
This example uses data from the mass spectrum of zirconium.

	A	B	C
1	Relative Isotopic Mass	Relative Abundance	Relative Mass × Abundance
2	90	100.00	9000.00
3	91	21.81	1984.71
4	92	33.33	3066.36
5	94	33.78	3175.32
6	96	5.44	522.24
7		**194.36**	**17748.63**
8			
9	Relative Atomic Mass =		91.31833
10			

In this column, the spreadsheet has multiplied the numbers in column A by the numbers in column B to give the **product** of each **relative isotopic mass** and its **relative abundance**.

In these cells, the spreadsheet has **added** up the numbers in the cells above to give the two totals you need to calculate the A_r.

To work out the **relative atomic mass**, the sum in cell C7 is **divided** by the sum in B7. So the relative atomic mass of zirconium is 91.3, to 1 decimal place.

Practice Questions

Q1 Explain what relative atomic mass (A_r) and relative isotopic mass mean.

Q2 Explain the difference between relative molecular mass and relative formula mass.

Q3 Explain what relative isotopic abundance means.

Q4 Explain why the relative atomic mass is rarely a whole number.

Exam Questions

Q1 Copper exists in two main isotopic forms, ^{63}Cu and ^{65}Cu.
 a) Calculate the relative atomic mass of copper using the information
 from the mass spectrum. [2 marks]
 b) Explain why the relative atomic mass of copper is not a whole number. [2 marks]

Q2 The percentage make-up of naturally occurring potassium is 93.11 % ^{39}K, 0.12 % ^{40}K and 6.77 % ^{41}K.
 Use the information to determine the relative atomic mass of potassium. [2 marks]

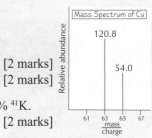

You can't pick your relatives, you just have to learn them...

Working out A_r is dead easy — and using a spreadsheet makes it even easier. It'll really help if you know the mass numbers for the first 20 elements or so, or you'll spend half your time looking back at the periodic table. I hope you've done the Practice Questions, cos they pretty much cover the rest of the stuff, and if you can get them right, you've nailed it.

The Mole

It'd be handy to be able to count out atoms — but they're way too tiny. You can't even see them, never mind get hold of them with tweezers. But not to worry — using the idea of relative mass, you can figure out how many atoms you've got.

A **Mole** is Just a (Very Large) **Number of Particles**

Chemists often talk about 'amount of substance'. Basically, all they mean is 'number of particles'.

1) Amount of substance is measured using a unit called the **mole** (**mol** for short) and given the symbol n.

2) One mole is roughly **6.02×10^{23} particles** (**the Avogadro constant, N_A**).

3) It **doesn't matter** what the particles are.
   They can be atoms, molecules, penguins — **anything**.

4) Here's a nice simple formula for finding the number of moles from the number of atoms or molecules:

$$\text{Number of moles} = \frac{\text{Number of particles you have}}{\text{Number of particles in a mole}}$$

> **Example:** I have 1.5×10^{24} carbon atoms. How many moles of carbon is this?
>
> $$\text{Number of moles} = \frac{1.5 \times 10^{24}}{6.02 \times 10^{23}} \approx 2.49 \text{ moles}$$

Molar Mass is the Mass of One Mole

Molar mass, M, is the mass of **one mole** of something.

But the main thing to remember is:

> Molar mass is just the same as the relative molecular mass, M_r

That's why the mole is such a ridiculous number of particles (6.02×10^{23}) — it's the number of particles for which the weight in g is the same as the relative molecular mass.

The only difference is you stick a 'g mol^{-1}' on the end...

> **Example:** Find the molar mass of $CaCO_3$.
>
> Relative formula mass, M_r, of $CaCO_3 = 40 + 12 + (3 \times 16) = 100$
> So the molar mass, M, is **100 g mol^{-1}**. — i.e. 1 mole of $CaCO_3$ weighs 100 g.

Here's another formula. This one's really important — you need it **all the time**:

$$\text{Number of moles} = \frac{\text{mass of substance}}{\text{molar mass}}$$

> **Example:** How many moles of aluminium oxide are present in 5.1 g of Al_2O_3?
>
> Molar mass of Al_2O_3 = $(2 \times 27) + (3 \times 16)$
> = 102 g mol^{-1}
>
> Number of moles of Al_2O_3 = $\frac{5.1}{102}$ = **0.05 moles**

> **Example:** How many moles of chlorine molecules are present in 71 g of chlorine gas?
>
> We're talking chlorine **molecules** (not chlorine atoms), so it's Cl_2 we're interested in.
> Molar mass of Cl_2 = $(2 \times 35.5) = 71$ g mol^{-1}
>
> Number of moles of Cl_2 = $\frac{71}{71}$ = **1 mole**
>
> *But note that it would be **2 moles** of chlorine **atoms**, since chlorine **atoms** have a molar mass of 35.5 g mol^{-1}.*

The Mole

In a Solution the **Concentration** is Measured in **mol dm⁻³**

1) The **concentration** of a solution is how many **moles** are dissolved per **1 dm³** of solution. The units are **mol dm⁻³** (or **M**).

 $1 dm^3 = 1000 cm^3 = 1\ litre$

2) Here's the formula to find the **number of moles**.

$$\text{Number of moles} = \frac{\text{Concentration} \times \text{Volume (in cm}^3)}{1000}$$

or just

$$\text{Number of moles} = \text{Concentration} \times \text{Volume (in dm}^3)$$

> **Example:** What mass of sodium hydroxide needs to be dissolved to make 50 cm³ of a 2 M solution?
>
> $$\text{Number of moles} = \frac{2 \times 50}{1000} = 0.1 \text{ moles of NaOH}$$
>
> Molar mass, M, of NaOH = 23 + 16 + 1 = 40 g mol⁻¹
>
> $$\text{Mass} = \text{number of moles} \times M = 0.1 \times 40 = \textbf{4 g}$$

3) A solution that has **more moles per dm³** than another is **more concentrated**.
A solution that has **fewer moles per dm³** than another is **more dilute**.

All Gases Take Up the **Same Volume** under the Same Conditions

If temperature and pressure stay the same, **one mole** of **any** gas always has the **same volume**.
At **room temperature and pressure** (r.t.p.), this happens to be **24 dm³**, (r.t.p is 298 K (25 °C) and 101.3 kPa).
Here are 2 formulas for working out the number of moles in a volume of gas. Don't forget — **ONLY** use them for r.t.p.

$$\text{Number of moles} = \frac{\text{Volume in dm}^3}{24} \qquad \text{OR} \qquad \text{Number of moles} = \frac{\text{Volume in cm}^3}{24\ 000}$$

> **Example:** How many moles are there in 6 dm³ of oxygen gas at r.t.p.?
>
> $$\text{Number of moles} = \frac{6}{24} = \textbf{0.25 moles of oxygen molecules}$$

Practice Questions

Q1 How many molecules are there in one mole of ethane molecules?

Q2 Which has the most particles, a solution of concentration 0.1 mol dm⁻³ or an equal volume of one that is 0.1 M?

Q3 What volume does 1 mole of gas occupy at r.t.p.?

Exam Questions

Q1 Calculate the mass of 0.36 moles of ethanoic acid, CH_3COOH. [2 marks]

Q2 What mass of H_2SO_4 is needed to produce 60 cm³ of 0.25 M solution? [2 marks]

Q3 What volume will be occupied by 88 g of propane gas (C_3H_8) at r.t.p.? [2 marks]

Put your back teeth on the scale and find out your molar mass...

You need this stuff for loads of the calculation questions you might get, so make sure you know it inside out. Before you start plugging numbers into formulas, make sure they're in the right units. If they're not, you need to know how to convert them or you'll be tossing marks out the window. Learn all the definitions and formulas, then have a bash at the questions.

Empirical and Molecular Formulas

Here's another page piled high with numbers — it's all just glorified maths really.

Empirical and Molecular Formulas are Ratios

You have to know what's what with empirical and molecular formulas, so here goes...

1) The **empirical formula** gives the smallest whole number ratio of atoms in a compound.
2) The **molecular formula** gives the **actual** numbers of atoms in a molecule.
3) The molecular formula is made up of a whole **number** of empirical units.

Example: A molecule has an empirical formula of $C_4H_3O_2$, and a molecular mass of 166 g. Work out its molecular formula.

First find the **empirical mass** —
$$(4 \times 12) + (3 \times 1) + (2 \times 16)$$
$$= 48 + 3 + 32 = 83 \text{ g}$$

Compare the empirical and molecular masses.

Empirical mass is just like the relative formula mass... (if that helps at all...).

But the **molecular mass** is 166 g,

so there are $\dfrac{166}{83} = 2$ empirical units in the molecule.

The molecular formula must be the **empirical formula × 2**, so the molecular formula = $C_8H_6O_4$. So there you go.

Empirical Formulas are Calculated from Experiments

You need to be able to work out empirical formulas from **experimental results** too.

Example: When a hydrocarbon is burnt in excess oxygen, 4.4 g of carbon dioxide and 1.8 g of water are made. What is the empirical formula of the hydrocarbon?

First work out how many moles of the products you have.

$$\text{No. of moles of } CO_2 = \frac{\text{mass}}{M} = \frac{4.4}{12 + (16 \times 2)} = \frac{4.4}{44} = 0.1 \text{ moles}$$

1 mole of CO_2 contains 1 mole of carbon atoms, so you must have started with **0.1 moles of carbon atoms**.

$$\text{No. of moles of } H_2O = \frac{1.8}{(2 \times 1) + 16} = \frac{1.8}{18} = 0.1 \text{ moles}$$

1 mole of H_2O contains 2 moles of hydrogen atoms (H), so you must have started with **0.2 moles of hydrogen atoms**.

Ratio C : H = 0.1 : 0.2 . Now you divide both numbers by the **smallest** — here it's 0.1.
So, the ratio C : H = 1 : 2. So the empirical formula must be CH_2.

This works because the only place the carbon in the carbon dioxide and the hydrogen in the water could have come from is the hydrocarbon.

As if that's not enough, you also need to know how to work out empirical formulas from the **percentages** of the different elements.

Example: A compound is found to have percentage composition 56.5% potassium, 8.7% carbon and 34.8% oxygen by mass. Calculate its empirical formula.

If you assume you've got 100 g of the compound, you can turn the % straight into mass, and then work out the number of moles as normal.

In **100 g** of compound there are:

Use $n = \dfrac{\text{mass}}{M}$

$\dfrac{56.5}{39} = 1.449$ moles of K $\dfrac{8.7}{12} = 0.725$ moles of C $\dfrac{34.8}{16} = 2.175$ moles of O

Divide each number of moles by the **smallest number** — in this case it's 0.725.

K: $\dfrac{1.449}{0.725} = 2.0$ C: $\dfrac{0.725}{0.725} = 1.0$ O: $\dfrac{2.175}{0.725} = 3.0$

The ratio of K : C : O = 2 : 1 : 3. So you know the empirical formula's got to be K_2CO_3.

Empirical and Molecular Formulas

Molecular Formulas are Calculated from Experimental Data Too

Once you know the empirical formula, you just need a bit more info and you can work out the **molecular formula** too.

Example:

When 4.6 g of an alcohol, with molar mass 46 g, is burnt in excess oxygen,
it produces 8.8 g of carbon dioxide and 5.4 g of water.
Calculate the empirical formula for the alcohol and then its molecular formula.

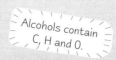
Alcohols contain C, H and O.

The carbon in the CO_2 and the hydrogen in the H_2O must have come from the alcohol — work out the number of moles of each of these.

No. of moles of $CO_2 = \dfrac{\text{mass}}{M} = \dfrac{8.8}{44} = 0.2$ moles

1 mole of CO_2 contains 1 mole of C. So, 0.2 moles of CO_2 contains **0.2 moles of C**.

No. of moles $H_2O = \dfrac{\text{mass}}{M} = \dfrac{5.4}{18} = 0.3$ moles

1 mole of H_2O contains 2 moles of H. So, 0.3 moles of H_2O contain **0.6 moles of H**.

Mass of C = no. of moles × M = 0.2 × 12 = 2.4 g
Mass of H = no. of moles × M = 0.6 × 1 = 0.6 g
Mass of O = 4.6 – (2.4 + 0.6) = 1.6 g

Number of moles O = $\dfrac{\text{mass}}{M} = \dfrac{1.6}{16} = 0.1$ moles

Now work out the mass of carbon and hydrogen in the alcohol. The rest of the mass of the alcohol must be oxygen — so work out that too. Once you know the mass of O, you can work out how many moles there are of it.

Molar Ratio = C : H : O = 0.2 : 0.6 : 0.1 = 2 : 6 : 1
Empirical formula = C_2H_6O

When you know the number of moles of each element, you've got the molar ratio. Divide each number by the smallest.

Mass of empirical formula = (12 × 2) + (1 × 6) + 16 = 46 g

Compare the empirical and molecular masses.

In this example, the mass of the empirical formula equals the molecular mass, so the empirical and molecular formulas are the same.
Molecular formula = C_2H_6O

Practice Questions

Q1 Define 'empirical formula'.

Q2 What is the difference between a molecular formula and an empirical formula?

Exam Questions

Q1 Hydrocarbon X has a molecular mass of 78 g. It is found to have 92.3% carbon and 7.7% hydrogen by mass. Calculate the empirical and molecular formulae of X. [3 marks]

Q2 When 1.2 g of magnesium ribbon is heated in air, it burns to form a white powder, which has a mass of 2 g. What is the empirical formula of the powder? [2 marks]

Q3 When 19.8 g of an organic acid, A, is burnt in excess oxygen,
33 g of carbon dioxide and 10.8 g of water are produced.
Calculate the empirical formula for A and hence its molecular formula, if $M_r(A) = 132$.

Hint: organic acids contain C, H and O.

[4 marks]

The Empirical Strikes Back...

With this stuff, it's not enough to learn a few facts parrot-fashion, to regurgitate in the exam — you've gotta know how to use them. The only way to do that is to practise. Go through all the examples on these two pages again, this time working the answers out for yourself. Then test yourself on the practice exam questions. It'll help you sleep at night — honest.

Equations and Calculations

Balancing equations'll cause you a few palpitations — as soon as you make one bit right, the rest goes pear-shaped.

Balanced Equations have **Equal Numbers** of each Atom on **Both Sides**

1) Balanced equations have the **same number** of each atom on **both** sides. They're... well... you know... balanced.

2) You can only add more atoms by adding **whole compounds**. You do this by putting a number **in front** of a compound or changing one that's already there. You **can't** mess with formulas — ever.

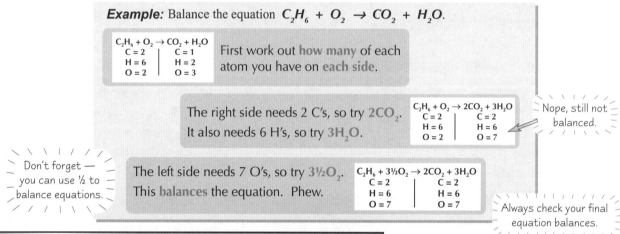

Example: Balance the equation $C_2H_6 + O_2 \rightarrow CO_2 + H_2O$.

$C_2H_6 + O_2 \rightarrow CO_2 + H_2O$

C = 2	C = 1
H = 6	H = 2
O = 2	O = 3

First work out **how many** of each atom you have on **each side**.

The right side needs 2 C's, so try $2CO_2$. It also needs 6 H's, so try $3H_2O$.

$C_2H_6 + O_2 \rightarrow 2CO_2 + 3H_2O$

C = 2	C = 2
H = 6	H = 6
O = 2	O = 7

Nope, still not balanced.

Don't forget — you can use ½ to balance equations.

The left side needs 7 O's, so try $3\frac{1}{2}O_2$. This **balances** the equation. Phew.

$C_2H_6 + 3\frac{1}{2}O_2 \rightarrow 2CO_2 + 3H_2O$

C = 2	C = 2
H = 6	H = 6
O = 7	O = 7

Always check your final equation balances.

In **Ionic Equations** the **Charges** must Balance too

In ionic equations, only the **reacting particles** are included. You don't have to worry about the rest of the stuff.

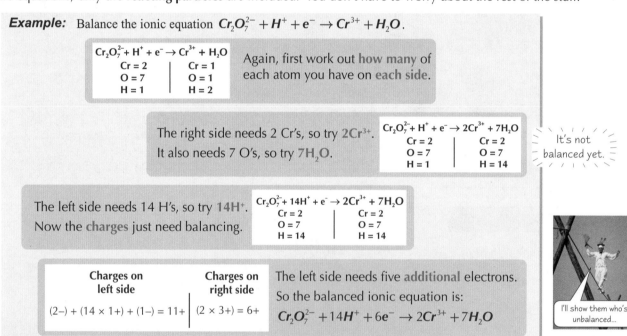

Example: Balance the ionic equation $Cr_2O_7^{2-} + H^+ + e^- \rightarrow Cr^{3+} + H_2O$.

$Cr_2O_7^{2-} + H^+ + e^- \rightarrow Cr^{3+} + H_2O$

Cr = 2	Cr = 1
O = 7	O = 1
H = 1	H = 2

Again, first work out **how many** of each atom you have on **each side**.

The right side needs 2 Cr's, so try $2Cr^{3+}$. It also needs 7 O's, so try $7H_2O$.

$Cr_2O_7^{2-} + H^+ + e^- \rightarrow 2Cr^{3+} + 7H_2O$

Cr = 2	Cr = 2
O = 7	O = 7
H = 1	H = 14

It's not balanced yet.

The left side needs 14 H's, so try **14H⁺**. Now the **charges** just need balancing.

$Cr_2O_7^{2-} + 14H^+ + e^- \rightarrow 2Cr^{3+} + 7H_2O$

Cr = 2	Cr = 2
O = 7	O = 7
H = 14	H = 14

Charges on left side	Charges on right side
$(2-) + (14 \times 1+) + (1-) = 11+$	$(2 \times 3+) = 6+$

The left side needs five **additional** electrons. So the balanced ionic equation is:

$$Cr_2O_7^{2-} + 14H^+ + 6e^- \rightarrow 2Cr^{3+} + 7H_2O$$

I'll show them who's unbalanced...

Balanced Equations can be used to Work out Masses

Example: Calculate the mass of iron oxide produced if 28 g of iron is burnt in air.

$$2Fe + \tfrac{3}{2}O_2 \rightarrow Fe_2O_3$$

The molar mass, M, of Fe = 56 g, so the number of moles in 28 g of Fe = $\dfrac{mass}{M} = \dfrac{28}{56} = 0.5$ moles

From the equation: 2 moles of Fe produces 1 mole of Fe_2O_3, so 0.5 moles of Fe produces 0.25 moles of Fe_2O_3.

Once you know the number of moles and the molar mass (M) of Fe_2O_3, it's easy to work out the mass.

M of $Fe_2O_3 = (2 \times 56) + (3 \times 16) = 160$ g mol⁻¹

Mass of Fe_2O_3 = no. of moles × M = 0.25 × 160 = **40 g**. And that's your answer.

Equations and Calculations

That's not all... *Balanced Equations* can be used to *Work Out Gas Volumes*

It's pretty handy to be able to work out **how much gas** a reaction will produce, so that you can use **large enough apparatus**. Or else there might be a rather large bang.

Example: How much gas is produced when 15 g of sodium is reacted with excess water at r.t.p.?

$$2Na_{(s)} + 2H_2O_{(l)} \rightarrow 2NaOH_{(aq)} + H_{2(g)}$$

M of Na = 23 g mol^{-1}, so number of moles in 15 g of Na = $\frac{15}{23}$ = 0.65 moles

Excess water means you know all the sodium will react.

From the equation, 2 moles Na produces 1 mole H$_2$,

so you know 0.65 moles Na produces $\frac{0.65}{2}$ = 0.325 moles H$_2$.

So the volume of H$_2$ = 0.325 × 24 = **7.8 dm³**

The reaction happens at room temperature and pressure, so you know 1 mole takes up 24 dm³.

State Symbols Give a bit More Information about the Substances

State symbols are put after each compound in an equation. They tell you what **state of matter** things are in.

s = solid
l = liquid
g = gas
aq = aqueous
    (solution in water)

To show you what I mean, here's an example —

$$CaCO_{3\,(s)} + 2HCl_{(aq)} \rightarrow CaCl_{2\,(aq)} + H_2O_{(l)} + CO_{2\,(g)}$$

solid   solution   solution   liquid   gas

Practice Questions

Q1 What is the state symbol for a solution of hydrochloric acid?

Q2 What is the difference between a balanced equation and an ionic equation?

Exam Questions

Q1 Calculate the mass of ethene required to produce 258 g of chloroethane, C_2H_5Cl.

$$C_2H_4 + HCl \rightarrow C_2H_5Cl$$

[4 marks]

Q2 15 g of calcium carbonate is heated strongly so that it fully decomposes. $CaCO_{3(s)} \rightarrow CaO_{(s)} + CO_{2(g)}$

a) Calculate the mass of calcium oxide produced.   [3 marks]

b) Calculate the volume of gas produced.   [3 marks]

Q3 Balance this equation: $KI + Pb(NO_3)_2 \rightarrow PbI_2 + 2KNO_3$ [1 mark]

Don't get in a state about equations...

You're probably completely fed up with all these equations, calculations, moles and whatnot... well hang in there — there are just a few more pages coming up. I've said it once, and I'll say it again — practise, practise, practise... it's the only road to salvation (by the way, where is salvation anyway?). Keep going... you're nearly there.

Acids, Bases and Salts

Acid's a word that's thrown around willy-nilly — but now for the truth...

Acids are all about Hydrated Protons

1) When mixed with **water**, all acids **release hydrogen ions** — H^+ (these are just **protons**, but you never get them by themselves in water — they're always combined with H_2O to form hydroxonium ions, H_3O^+).

$$H_2SO_{4(l)} + water \rightarrow 2H^+_{(aq)} + SO_4^{2-}_{(aq)}$$
$$HCl_{(g)} + water \rightarrow H^+_{(aq)} + Cl^-_{(aq)}$$

2) **Bases** do the opposite — they want to **grab H^+ ions**.

So,
> **Acids** produce $H^+_{(aq)}$ ions in an aqueous solution — i.e. they're **proton donors**.
> **Bases** remove $H^+_{(aq)}$ ions from an aqueous solution — i.e. they're **proton acceptors**.

HCl doesn't release hydrogen ions until it meets water — so hydrogen chloride gas isn't an acid.

Acids React to Form Neutral Salts

1) Acid molecules release their hydrogen ions, so **other ions** can hop into their places. You get a **salt** if the hydrogen ions are replaced by **metal ions** or **ammonium (NH_4^+) ions**.

2) Different acids produce **different salts** — sulfuric acid (H_2SO_4) produces salts called **sulfates**, hydrochloric acid (HCl) produces **chlorides**, and nitric acid (HNO_3) produces **nitrates**.

Learn the formulas of these three acids.

3) Not only that, but there are a few different things acids can react with that result in salts — read on...

Acids React with Bases

1) When **acids** react with **bases**, they **neutralise** each other.

2) **Metal oxides**, **metal hydroxides** and **ammonia** are common bases. An **alkali** is just a base that dissolves in water. **Sodium hydroxide (NaOH)** and **potassium hydroxide (KOH)** are the alkalis you're most likely to meet.

3) Alkalis **release OH^- ions** in water. These OH^- ions accept H^+ **ions** (protons) from an acid to form **water molecules**.

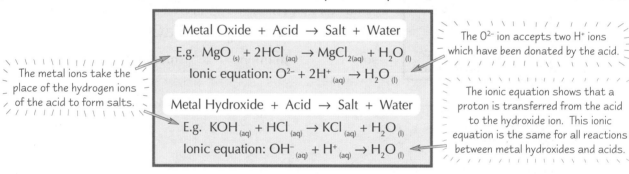

The metal ions take the place of the hydrogen ions of the acid to form salts.

> Metal Oxide + Acid $\rightarrow$ Salt + Water
> E.g. $MgO_{(s)} + 2HCl_{(aq)} \rightarrow MgCl_{2(aq)} + H_2O_{(l)}$
> Ionic equation: $O^{2-} + 2H^+_{(aq)} \rightarrow H_2O_{(l)}$
>
> Metal Hydroxide + Acid $\rightarrow$ Salt + Water
> E.g. $KOH_{(aq)} + HCl_{(aq)} \rightarrow KCl_{(aq)} + H_2O_{(l)}$
> Ionic equation: $OH^-_{(aq)} + H^+_{(aq)} \rightarrow H_2O_{(l)}$

The O^{2-} ion accepts two H^+ ions which have been donated by the acid.

The ionic equation shows that a proton is transferred from the acid to the hydroxide ion. This ionic equation is the same for all reactions between metal hydroxides and acids.

4) Ammonia, NH_3, is a **base** — in fact it dissolves in water, so **aqueous ammonia** is an **alkali**. It'll happily **accept a proton** from an acid to form an **ammonium ion** — this can then form an **ammonium salt**.

Here's how ammonia reacts with nitric acid (HNO_3) and sulfuric acid

$$NH_{3(aq)} + HNO_{3(aq)} \rightarrow NH_4NO_{3(aq)}$$
$$2NH_{3(aq)} + H_2SO_{4(aq)} \rightarrow (NH_4)_2SO_{4(aq)}$$

$$NH_{3(aq)} + H^+_{(aq)} \rightarrow NH_4^+_{(aq)}$$

And here's the ionic equation. It's dead useful because it applies to all reactions of ammonia with acids.

Acids can React with Metals and Carbonates too

When acids react with **metals** and **carbonates**, **salts** are produced.

> Metal + Acid $\rightarrow$ Metal Salt + Hydrogen
> E.g. $Mg_{(s)} + H_2SO_{4(aq)} \rightarrow MgSO_{4(aq)} + H_{2(g)}$
> Or the ionic equation: $Mg_{(s)} + 2H^+_{(aq)} \rightarrow Mg^{2+}_{(aq)} + H_{2(g)}$
>
> Metal Carbonate + Acid $\rightarrow$ Metal Salt + Carbon Dioxide + Water
> E.g. $Na_2CO_{3(s)} + 2HCl_{(aq)} \rightarrow 2NaCl_{(aq)} + CO_{2(g)} + H_2O_{(l)}$
> Ionic equation: $CO_3^{2-}_{(s)} + 2H^+_{(aq)} \rightarrow CO_{2(g)} + H_2O_{(l)}$

Professor Redmond's final classroom demonstration...

Effects of submersion in a bath of conc. H_2SO_4.

Acids, Bases and Salts

Salts *Can Be* **Anhydrous** *or* **Hydrated**

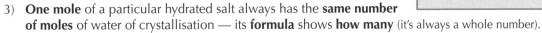

1) All solid salts consist of a **lattice** of positive and negative ions. In some salts, **water molecules** are incorporated in the lattice too.

> Here's a tiny part of the lattice in a hydrated salt.
>
> Water molecules are **polar** (see p34). They're held in place in the lattice because they're attracted to the ions.

2) The water in a lattice is called **water of crystallisation**. A solid salt containing water of crystallisation is **hydrated**. A salt is **anhydrous** if it doesn't contain water of crystallisation.

3) **One mole** of a particular hydrated salt always has the **same number of moles** of water of crystallisation — its **formula** shows **how many** (it's always a whole number).

4) For example, **hydrated copper sulfate** has **five** moles of water for every mole of the salt. So its formula is $CuSO_4.5H_2O$. ⟵ Notice that there's a dot between $CuSO_4$ and $5H_2O$.

5) Many hydrated salts **lose** their water of crystallisation **when heated**, to become **anhydrous**. If you know the mass of the salt when hydrated and anhydrous, you can work its formula out like this:

> **Example:** Heating 3.210 g of hydrated magnesium sulfate, $MgSO_4.XH_2O$, forms 1.567 g of anhydrous magnesium sulfate. Find the value of **X** and write the formula of the hydrated salt.
>
> First you find the number of moles of water lost.
>
> | | | |
> |---|---|---|
> | Mass of water lost: | $3.210 - 1.567$ | $= 1.643$ g |
> | Number of moles of water lost: | mass ÷ molar mass = 1.643 g ÷ 18 | = **0.0913 moles** |
>
> Then you find the number of moles of anhydrous salt.
>
> | | | |
> |---|---|---|
> | Molar mass of $MgSO_4$: | $24 + 32 + (4 \times 16)$ | $= 120$ g mol^{-1} |
> | Number of moles (in 1.567 g): | mass ÷ molar mass = 1.567 ÷ 120 | = **0.0131 moles** |
>
> Now you work out the ratio of moles of anhydrous salt to moles of water in the form 1 : n.
>
> From the experiment, **0.0131 moles of salt : 0.0913 moles of water**,
>
> So, 1 mole of salt : $\dfrac{0.0913}{0.0131} = 6.97$ **moles of water**.
>
> *You might be given the percentage of the mass that is water — use the method on p12.*
>
> X must be a whole number, and some errors are to be expected in any experiment, so you can safely round off your result — so the formula of the hydrated salt is $MgSO_4.7H_2O$.

Practice Questions

Q1 Write an ionic equation for the reaction between a metal hydroxide and an acid.

Q2 Explain what an alkali is.

Q3 Why can water molecules become fixed in an ionic lattice?

Exam Questions

Q1 Chloric(VII) acid, $HClO_4$, and sulfuric acid, H_2SO_4, are both strong acids.
   a) Write a balanced equation, including state symbols, for the reaction between chloric(VII) acid and calcium carbonate, $CaCO_3$.   [3 marks]
   b) Sulfuric acid reacts with lithium metal, potassium hydroxide and ammonia.
      (i) Write an ionic equation for the reaction with lithium.   [2 marks]
      (ii) Write an equation for the reaction with potassium hydroxide.   [2 marks]
      (iii) Write an equation for the reaction with aqueous ammonia.   [2 marks]

Q2 A sample of hydrated calcium sulfate, $CaSO_4.XH_2O$, was prepared by reacting calcium hydroxide with sulfuric acid. 1.883 g of hydrated salt was produced. This was then heated until all the water of crystallisation was driven off and the product was then reweighed. Its mass was 1.133 g.
   a) How many moles of anhydrous calcium sulfate were produced?   [2 marks]
   b) What mass of water was present in the hydrated salt?   [1 mark]
   c) Calculate the value of **X** in the formula $CaSO_4.XH_2O$. (**X** is an integer.)   [3 marks]

It's a stick-up — your protons or your life...

Remember — all acids have protons to give away and bases just love to take them. It's what makes them acids and bases. It's like how bus drivers drive buses... it's what makes them bus drivers. Learn the formulas for the common acids — hydrochloric, sulfuric and nitric, and the common alkalis — sodium hydroxide, potassium hydroxide and aqueous ammonia.

Titrations

*Titrations are used to find out the **concentrations** of acid or alkali solutions.*
They're also handy when you're making salts of soluble bases.

Titrations need to be done **Accurately**

1) **Titrations** allow you to find out **exactly** how much acid is needed to **neutralise** a quantity of alkali.

2) You measure out some **alkali** using a pipette and put it in a flask, along with some **indicator**, e.g. **phenolphthalein**.

3) First of all, do a rough titration to get an idea where the **end point** is (the point where the alkali is **exactly neutralised** and the indicator changes colour). Add the **acid** to the alkali using a **burette** — giving the flask a regular **swirl**.

4) Now do an **accurate** titration. Run the acid in to within 2 cm³ of the end point, then add the acid **dropwise**. If you don't notice exactly when the solution changed colour you've **overshot** and your result won't be accurate.

5) **Record** the amount of acid used to **neutralise** the alkali. It's best to **repeat** this process a few times, making sure you get the same answer each time.

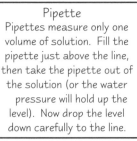

Pipette
Pipettes measure only one volume of solution. Fill the pipette just above the line, then take the pipette out of the solution (or the water pressure will hold up the level). Now drop the level down carefully to the line.

You can also do titrations the other way round — adding alkali to acid.

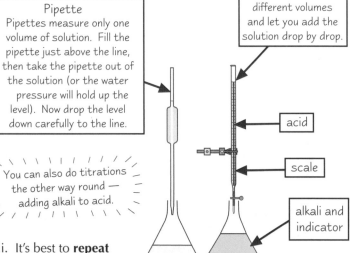

Burette
Burettes measure different volumes and let you add the solution drop by drop.

acid

scale

alkali and indicator

Indicators Show you when the Reaction's Just Finished

Indicators change **colour**, as if by magic. In titrations, indicators that change colour quickly over a **very small pH range** are used so you know **exactly** when the reaction has ended.

The main two indicators for **acid/alkali reactions** are —

> **methyl orange** — turns **yellow** to **red** when adding acid to alkali.
> **phenolphthalein** — turns **red** to **colourless** when adding acid to alkali.

Choppy seas made it difficult for Captain Blackbird to read the burette accurately.

Universal indicator is no good here — its colour change is too gradual.

You can Calculate **Concentrations** from Titrations

Now for the calculations...

> **Example:** 25 cm³ of 0.5 M HCl was used to neutralise 35 cm³ of NaOH solution.
> Calculate the concentration of the sodium hydroxide solution in mol dm⁻³.
>
> First write a **balanced equation** and decide **what you know** and what you **need to know**:
>
> $$HCl + NaOH \rightarrow NaCl + H_2O$$
> $$25 \text{ cm}^3 \quad\quad 35 \text{ cm}^3$$
> $$0.5 \text{ M} \quad\quad\quad ?$$
>
> *It's just the formula from page 11.*
>
> Now work out how many **moles of HCl** you have:
>
> $$\text{Number of moles HCl} = \frac{\text{concentration} \times \text{volume (cm}^3)}{1000} = \frac{0.5 \times 25}{1000} = 0.0125 \text{ moles}$$
>
> From the equation, you know 1 mole of HCl neutralises 1 mole of NaOH.
> So 0.0125 moles of HCl must neutralise **0.0125** moles of NaOH.
>
> Now it's a doddle to work out the **concentration of NaOH**.
>
> $$\text{Concentration of NaOH}_{(aq)} = \frac{\text{moles of NaOH} \times 1000}{\text{volume (cm}^3)} = \frac{0.0125 \times 1000}{35} = 0.36 \text{ mol dm}^{-3}$$

Titrations

You use a *Pretty Similar Method* to Calculate *Volumes* for Reactions

This is usually used for **planning experiments**.

You need to use this formula again, but this time **rearrange** it to find the volume. ⟶ $$\text{number of moles} = \frac{\text{concentration} \times \text{volume (cm}^3)}{1000}$$

Example: 20.4 cm³ of a 0.5 M solution of sodium carbonate reacts with 1.5 M nitric acid. Calculate the volume of nitric acid required to neutralise the sodium carbonate.

First write a **balanced equation** for the reaction and decide **what you know** and what you **want to know**:

$$Na_2CO_3 + 2HNO_3 \rightarrow 2NaNO_3 + H_2O + CO_2$$

20.4 cm³   ?

0.5 M   1.5 M

Now work out how many **moles** of Na_2CO_3 you've got:

$$\text{No. of moles of } Na_2CO_3 = \frac{\text{concentration} \times \text{volume (cm}^3)}{1000} = \frac{0.5 \times 20.4}{1000} = 0.0102 \text{ moles}$$

1 mole of Na_2CO_3 neutralises 2 moles of HNO_3, so 0.0102 moles of Na_2CO_3 neutralises **0.0204 moles of HNO_3**.

Now you know the number of moles of HNO_3 and the concentration, you can work out the **volume**:

$$\text{Volume of } HNO_3 = \frac{\text{number of moles} \times 1000}{\text{concentration}} = \frac{0.0204 \times 1000}{1.5} = 13.6 \text{ cm}^3$$

Practice Questions

Q1 Describe the procedure for doing a titration.

Q2 What colour change would you expect to see if you added enough hydrochloric acid to a conical flask containing sodium hydroxide and methyl orange?

Exam Questions

Q1 Calculate the concentration (in M) of a solution of ethanoic acid, CH_3COOH, if 25.4 cm³ of it is neutralised by 14.6 cm³ of 0.5 M sodium hydroxide solution. $CH_3COOH + NaOH \rightarrow CH_3COONa + H_2O$ [3 marks]

Q2 You are supplied with 0.75 g of calcium carbonate and a solution of 0.25 M sulfuric acid. What volume of acid will be needed to neutralise the calcium carbonate? $CaCO_3 + H_2SO_4 \rightarrow CaSO_4 + H_2O + CO_2$ [4 marks]

Burettes and pipettes — big glass things, just waiting to be dropped...

Titrations are annoyingly fiddly. But you do get to use big, impressive-looking equipment and feel like you're doing something important. It's really tempting to rush it and let half the acid gush into the alkali first. But it's totally not worth it, cos you'll just have to do it again. Yep, this is definitely one of those slow-and-steady-wins-the-race situations.

Oxidation and Reduction

This double page has more occurrences of "oxidation" than the Beatles' "All You Need is Love" features the word "love".

If Electrons are Transferred, it's a Redox Reaction

1) A **loss** of electrons is called **oxidation**. A **gain** in electrons is called **reduction**.
2) Reduction and oxidation happen **simultaneously** — hence the term "**redox**" reaction.
3) An **oxidising agent accepts** electrons and gets reduced.
4) A **reducing agent donates** electrons and gets oxidised.

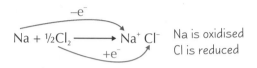

$$Na + \tfrac{1}{2}Cl_2 \longrightarrow Na^+ Cl^-$$

Na is oxidised
Cl is reduced

Sometimes it's easier to talk about Oxidation Numbers

(It's also called oxidation <u>state</u>.)

There are lots of rules. Take a deep breath...

1) All atoms are treated as **ions** for this, even if they're covalently bonded.

2) Uncombined **elements** have an oxidation number of **0**.

3) Elements just bonded to **identical atoms**, like O_2 and H_2, also have an oxidation number of **0**.

4) The oxidation number of a simple **monatomic ion**, e.g. Na^+, is the same as its **charge**.

5) In **compounds** or **compound ions**, the **overall oxidation number** is just the ion charge.

   SO_4^{2-} — **overall oxidation number = –2**,
   oxidation number of O = –2 (total = –8),
   so oxidation number of S = +6

   Within an ion, the most electronegative element (see p34) has a negative oxidation number (equal to its ionic charge). Other elements have more positive oxidation numbers.

6) The sum of the oxidation numbers for a **neutral compound** is 0.

   Fe_2O_3 — **overall oxidation number = 0**, oxidation number of O = –2
   (total = –6), so oxidation number of **Fe = +3**

7) Combined **oxygen** is –2 (except in O_2 where it's 0).

   There are a few exceptions to these but you don't need to know about them.

8) Combined **hydrogen** is +1 (except in H_2 where it's 0).

If you see **Roman numerals** in a chemical name, it's an **oxidation number**.
E.g. copper has oxidation number **+2** in **copper(II) sulfate**.

You Can Work Out Oxidation Numbers from Formulas or Systematic Names

Systematic names make the oxidation numbers of all the atoms making up a compound ion clear.

1) Ions with names ending in **-ate** (e.g. sulfate, nitrate, carbonate) contain **oxygen**, as well as another element. For example, **sulfates** contain **sulfur** and **oxygen**, **nitrates** contain **nitrogen** and **oxygen**... and so on.

2) But sometimes the 'other' element in the ion can exist with different oxidation numbers, and so form different '-ate ions'. In these cases, the oxidation number is attached as a Roman numeral.
   E.g., **sulfate(VI)** tells you that the **sulfur** has oxidation number **+6** — this is the SO_4^{2-} ion.
   However, in the **sulfate(IV)** ion, **sulfur** has oxidation number **+4** — this is the SO_3^{2-} ion.

   The oxidation number applies to the sulfur not the oxygen, because oxygen is always –2.

   Several ions have widely used common names that are different from their correct systematic names.
   For example, the <u>sulfate(IV)</u> ion (SO_3^{2-}) is often called the <u>sulfite</u> ion.

3) You might have to work out the systematic name for a compound, given its formula — e.g. KNO_3.
   Okay... it's potassium nitrate, but you need to give the **oxidation number** of the **nitrogen**. Here's how...

   You know that potassium **always** forms K^+ ions, so the charge on the **nitrate** ion must be **–1**. Each **oxygen** atom in the NO_3^- ion has oxidation number **–2**. This gives $3 \times -2 = -6$. Then, since the ion has an overall number of –1, the nitrogen must be in the **+5** state. So the compound is **potassium nitrate(V)**.

   NO_3^- is called the nitrate(V) ion.

Oxidation and Reduction

Oxidation Numbers go **Up** or **Down** as Electrons are **Lost** or **Gained**

1) The oxidation number for an atom will **increase by 1** for each **electron lost**.

2) The oxidation number will **decrease by 1** for each **electron gained**.

3) When **metals** form compounds, they generally **donate** electrons to form **positive ions** — meaning they usually have **positive oxidation numbers**.

4) When **non-metals** form compounds, they generally **gain** electrons — meaning they usually have **negative oxidation numbers**.

5) In a **redox** reaction, some oxidation numbers will **change** — like in this reaction between iron(III) oxide and **carbon(II) oxide** (aka carbon monoxide). The products are the element iron and **carbon(IV) oxide** (more commonly known as carbon dioxide).

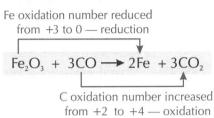

Fe oxidation number reduced from +3 to 0 — reduction

$$Fe_2O_3 + 3CO \longrightarrow 2Fe + 3CO_2$$

C oxidation number increased from +2 to +4 — oxidation

Many **Metals Reduce Dilute Acids**

1) On page 16 you saw how metals react with acids to produce a salt and hydrogen gas. Well this is a redox reaction:

- The metal atoms are **oxidised**, losing electrons and forming soluble metal ions.
- The hydrogen ions in solution are **reduced**, gaining electrons and forming hydrogen molecules.

2) For example, magnesium reacts with dilute hydrochloric acid like this:

Hands up if you like Roman numerals...

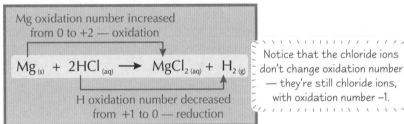

Mg oxidation number increased from 0 to +2 — oxidation

$$Mg_{(s)} + 2HCl_{(aq)} \longrightarrow MgCl_{2\,(aq)} + H_{2\,(g)}$$

H oxidation number decreased from +1 to 0 — reduction

Notice that the chloride ions don't change oxidation number — they're still chloride ions, with oxidation number –1.

3) If you use **sulfuric acid** instead of hydrochloric acid, exactly the same processes of **oxidation** and **reduction** take place. For example, potassium is oxidised to K^+ ions:

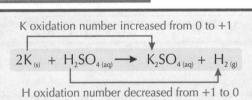

K oxidation number increased from 0 to +1

$$2K_{(s)} + H_2SO_{4\,(aq)} \longrightarrow K_2SO_{4\,(aq)} + H_{2\,(g)}$$

H oxidation number decreased from +1 to 0

Practice Questions

Q1 What is a reducing agent?

Q2 What is the usual oxidation number for oxygen combined with another element?

Q3 Explain why the systematic name of $NaNO_2$ is sodium nitrate(III).

Q4 Explain which element is oxidised and which is reduced in the reaction: $Ca + 2HCl \rightarrow CaCl_2 + H_2$

Exam Question

Q1 When hydrogen iodide gas is bubbled through warm concentrated sulfuric acid, hydrogen sulfide and iodine are produced.

a) Balance the equation below for the reaction.
$$H_2SO_{4\,(aq)} + HI_{\,(g)} \rightarrow H_2S_{\,(g)} + I_{2\,(s)} + H_2O_{\,(l)}$$
[1 mark]

b) State the oxidation number of sulfur in H_2SO_4 and in H_2S. [2 marks]

c) In this reaction, which is the reducing agent? Give a reason. [2 marks]

Redox — relax in a lovely warm bubble bath...

The thing here is to take your time. Questions on oxidation numbers aren't usually that hard, but they are easy to get wrong. So don't panic, take it easy, and get all the marks.

And while we're on the oxidation page, I suppose you ought to learn the most famous memory aid thingy in the world...

OIL RIG
- **O**xidation **I**s **L**oss
- **R**eduction **I**s **G**ain
(of electrons)

Electronic Structure

Those little electrons prancing about like mini bunnies decide what'll react with what — it's what chemistry's all about.

Electron Shells are Made Up of Sub-Shells and Orbitals

1) Electrons move around the nucleus in **shells** (sometimes called **energy levels**).
   These shells are all given numbers known as **principal quantum numbers**.

2) Shells **further** from the nucleus have a greater energy level than shells closer to the nucleus.

3) The shells contain different types of **sub-shell**. These sub-shells have different numbers of **orbitals**, which can each hold up to **2 electrons**.

This table shows the number of electrons that fit in each type of sub-shell.

Sub-shell	Number of orbitals	Maximum electrons
s	1	$1 \times 2 = 2$
p	3	$3 \times 2 = 6$
d	5	$5 \times 2 = 10$
f	7	$7 \times 2 = 14$

And this one shows the sub-shells and electrons in the first four energy levels.

Shell	Sub-shells	Total number or electrons	
1st	$1s$	2	= 2
2nd	$2s$ $2p$	$2 + (3 \times 2)$	= 8
3rd	$3s$ $3p$ $3d$	$2 + (3 \times 2) + (5 \times 2)$	= 18
4th	$4s$ $4p$ $4d$ $4f$	$2 + (3 \times 2) + (5 \times 2) + (7 \times 2)$	= 32

Orbitals Have Characteristic Shapes

There are a few things you need to know about orbitals... like what they are —

1) An orbital is the **bit of space** that an electron moves in. Orbitals within the same sub-shell have the **same energy**.

2) The electrons in the orbitals have to 'spin' in **opposite** directions — this is called **spin-pairing**.

3) s orbitals are **spherical** — p orbitals have **dumbbell shapes**. There are 3 p orbitals and they're at right angles to one another.

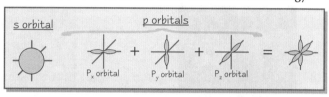

Work Out Electron Configurations by Filling the Lowest Energy Levels First

You can figure out most electronic configurations pretty easily, so long as you know a few simple rules —

1) Electrons fill up the **lowest** energy sub-shells first.

There's always got to be an exception to mess things up. The 4s sub-shell has a lower energy level than the 3d sub-shell, even though its principal quantum number is bigger. This means the 4s sub-shell fills up first.

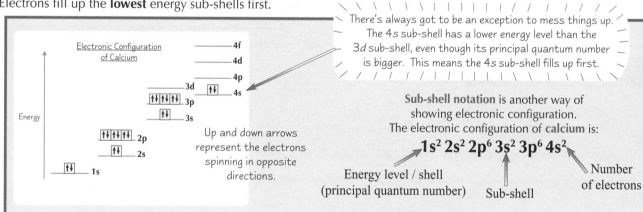

Up and down arrows represent the electrons spinning in opposite directions.

Sub-shell notation is another way of showing electronic configuration. The electronic configuration of **calcium** is:

$$1s^2\ 2s^2\ 2p^6\ 3s^2\ 3p^6\ 4s^2$$

Energy level / shell (principal quantum number)   Sub-shell   Number of electrons

2) Electrons fill orbitals **singly** before they start sharing. ⟶

See the next page for more on the s and p block.

3) For the configuration of **ions** from the **s** and **p** blocks of the periodic table, just **remove or add** the electrons to or from the highest-energy occupied sub-shell. E.g. $Mg^{2+} = 1s^2\ 2s^2\ 2p^6$, $Cl^- = 1s^2\ 2s^2\ 2p^6\ 3s^2\ 3p^6$

Watch out — **noble gas symbols**, like that of argon (Ar), are sometimes used in electron configurations. For example, calcium ($1s^2\ 2s^2\ 2p^6\ 3s^2\ 3p^6\ 4s^2$) can be written as [Ar]$4s^2$, where [Ar] = $1s^2\ 2s^2\ 2p^6\ 3s^2\ 3p^6$.

Electronic Structure

Electronic Structure Decides the **Chemical Properties** of an Element

The number of **outer shell electrons** decides the chemical properties of an element.

1) The **s block** elements (Groups 1 and 2) have 1 or 2 outer shell electrons.
   These are easily **lost** to form positive ions with an **inert gas configuration**.

> E.g. Na: $1s^2 2s^2 2p^6 3s^1 \rightarrow$ Na$^+$: $1s^2 2s^2 2p^6$ ◄

This is the electron configuration of neon.

2) The elements in Groups 5, 6 and 7 (in the p block) can **gain** 1, 2 or 3
   electrons to form negative ions with an **inert gas configuration**.

> E.g. O: $1s^2 2s^2 2p^4 \rightarrow$ O^{2-}: $1s^2 2s^2 2p^6$

Groups 4 to 7 can also **share** electrons when they form covalent bonds.

3) Group 0 (the inert gases) have **completely filled** s and p sub-shells
   and don't need to bother gaining, losing or sharing electrons
   — their full sub-shells make them **inert**.

4) The **d block** elements (which include the transition metals)
   tend to **lose** s and d electrons to form positive ions.

Sub-shells and the periodic table

Practice Questions

Q1 Write down the sub-shells in order of increasing energy up to 4p.

Q2 How many electrons do full s, p and d sub-shells contain?

Q3 Draw diagrams to show the shapes of an s and a p orbital.

Q4 What does the term 'spin-pairing' mean?

Exam Questions

Q1 Potassium reacts with oxygen to form potassium oxide, K$_2$O.

   a) Give the electron configurations of the K atom and K$^+$ ion.   [2 marks]

   b) Give the electron configuration of the oxygen atom.   [1 mark]

   c) Explain why it is the outer shell electrons, not those in the inner shells, which
   determine the chemistry of potassium and oxygen.   [2 marks]

Q2 This question concerns electron configurations in atoms and ions.

   a) What is the electron configuration of a manganese atom?   [1 mark]

   b) Identify the element with the 4th shell configuration of $4s^2 4p^2$.   [1 mark]

   c) Suggest the identity of an atom, a positive ion and a negative ion with the configuration $1s^2 2s^2 2p^6 3s^2 3p^6$.   [3 marks]

   d) Give the electron configuration of the Al^{3+} ion.   [1 mark]

She shells sub-sells on the shesore...

The way electrons fill up the orbitals is kind of like how strangers fill up seats on a bus. Everyone tends to sit in their own seat till they're forced to share. Except for the huge, scary man who comes and sits next to you. Make sure you learn the order that the sub-shells are filled up in, so you can write electron configurations for any atom or ion they throw at you.

Unit 1: Section 2 — Electrons, Bonding and Structure

Ionisation Energies

This page gets a trifle brain-boggling, so I hope you've got a few aspirin handy...

Ionisation *is the* Removal *of One or More* Electrons

When electrons have been removed from an atom or molecule, it's been **ionised**.
The energy you need to remove the first electron is called the **first ionisation energy**:

> The **first ionisation energy** is the energy needed to remove 1 electron from **each atom** in **1 mole** of **gaseous** atoms to form 1 mole of gaseous 1+ ions.

You have to put energy **in** to ionise an atom or molecule, so it's an **endothermic process**.

You can write **equations** for this process — here's the equation for the **first ionisation of oxygen**:

$$O_{(g)} \rightarrow O^+_{(g)} + e^- \quad \text{1st ionisation energy} = +1314 \text{ kJ mol}^{-1}$$

> Here are a few rather important points about ionisation energies:
> 1) You **must** use the gas state symbol, **(g)**, because ionisation energies are measured for gaseous atoms.
> 2) Always refer to **1 mole** of atoms, as stated in the definition, rather than to a single atom.
> 3) The **lower** the ionisation energy, the **easier** it is to form an ion.

The Factors *Affecting Ionisation Energy are...*

You need to know all about these...

 The **more protons** there are in the nucleus, the more positively charged the nucleus is and the **stronger the attraction** for the electrons.

 Attraction falls off very **rapidly with distance**. An electron **close** to the nucleus will be **much more** strongly attracted than one further away.

 As the number of electrons **between** the outer electrons and the nucleus **increases**, the outer electrons feel less attraction towards the nuclear charge. This lessening of the pull of the nucleus by inner shells of electrons is called **shielding (or screening)**.

> A **high ionisation energy** means there's a **high attraction** between the **electron** and the **nucleus**.

Successive Ionisation Energies *Involve Removing* Additional *Electrons*

1) You can remove **all** the electrons from an atom, leaving only the nucleus.
   Each time you remove an electron, there's a **successive ionisation energy**.
2) The definition for the **second ionisation energy** is:

> The **second ionisation energy** is the energy needed to remove 1 electron from **each ion** in **1 mole** of **gaseous** 1+ ions to form 1 mole of gaseous 2+ ions.

And here's the equation for the **second ionisation of oxygen** :

$$O^+_{(g)} \rightarrow O^{2+}_{(g)} + e^- \quad \text{2nd ionisation energy} = +3388 \text{ kJ mol}^{-1}$$

Ionisation Energies

Successive Ionisation Energies Show **Shell Structure**

If you have the successive ionisation energies of an element you can work out the number of electrons in each shell of the atom and which element the group is in.

A **graph** of successive ionisation energies (like this one for sodium) provides evidence for the **shell structure** of atoms.

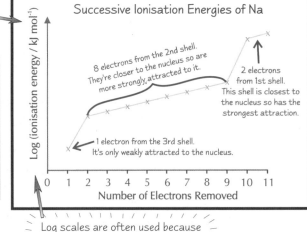

Successive Ionisation Energies of Na

Log (ionisation energy / kJ mol⁻¹)

8 electrons from the 2nd shell. They're closer to the nucleus so are more strongly attracted to it.

2 electrons from 1st shell. This shell is closest to the nucleus so has the strongest attraction.

1 electron from the 3rd shell. It's only weakly attracted to the nucleus.

Number of Electrons Removed

1) **Within each shell**, successive ionisation energies **increase**. This is because electrons are being removed from an **increasingly positive ion** — there's **less repulsion** amongst the remaining electrons, so they're **held more strongly** by the nucleus.

2) The **big jumps** in ionisation energy happen when a new shell is broken into — an electron is being removed from a shell **closer** to the nucleus.

1) Graphs like this can tell you which **group** of the periodic table an element belongs to. Just count **how many electrons are removed** before the first big jump to find the group number.

Log scales are often used because the values have such a huge range.

2) These graphs can be used to predict the **electronic structure** of an element. Working from **right to left**, count how many points there are before each big jump to find how many electrons are in each shell, starting with the first.

E.g. In the graph for sodium, **one electron** is removed before the first big jump — sodium is in **group 1**.

The graph has **2 points** on the right-hand side, then a jump, then **8 points**, a jump, and **1 final point**. Sodium has **2 electrons** in the first shell, **8** in the second and **1** in the third.

Practice Questions

Q1 Why is the (g) state symbol always used when writing ionisation energy equations?

Q2 Name three factors which affect the size of an ionisation energy.

Q3 Write the definition of the first and second ionisation energies.

Q4 Explain how you can tell that it's chlorine's successive ionisation energies that are shown on the graph on the right.

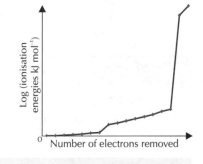

Log (ionisation energies kJ mol⁻¹)

Number of electrons removed

Exam Question

Q1 This graph shows the successive ionisation energies of a certain element.

a) To which group of the periodic table does this element belong? [1 mark]

b) Explain why it takes more energy to remove each successive electron. [2 marks]

c) What causes the sudden increases in ionisation energy? [1 mark]

d) What is the total number of shells of electrons in this element? [1 mark]

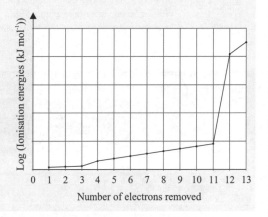

Log (Ionisation energies (kJ mol⁻¹))

Number of electrons removed

Shirt crumpled — ionise it...

When you're talking about ionisation energies in exams, always use the three main factors — shielding, nuclear charge and distance from nucleus. Make sure you're comfortable interpreting the jumps in those graphs without getting stressed. And recite the definitions of the first and second ionisation energies to yourself until the men in white coats get to you. Then stop.

Ionic Bonding

There are two main types of bonding — ionic and covalent. You need to make sure that you've got them both totally sussed.

Ionic Bonding is when Ions are Stuck Together by Electrostatic Attraction

1) Ions are formed when electrons are **transferred** from one atom to another.

2) The simplest ions are single atoms which have either lost or gained 1, 2 or 3 electrons so as to have a **full outer shell**.

> A sodium atom (Na) **loses** 1 electron to form a sodium ion (Na^+) $Na \rightarrow Na^+ + e^-$
> A magnesium atom (Mg) **loses** 2 electrons to form a magnesium ion (Mg^{2+}) $Mg \rightarrow Mg^{2+} + 2e^-$
> A chlorine atom (Cl) **gains** 1 electron to form a chloride ion (Cl^-) $Cl + e^- \rightarrow Cl^-$
> An oxygen atom (O) **gains** 2 electrons to form an oxide ion (O^{2-}) $O + 2e^- \rightarrow O^{2-}$

3) You **don't** have to remember what ion **each element** forms — nope, you just look at the Periodic Table. Elements in the same **group** all have the same number of **outer electrons**. So they have to **lose or gain** the same number to get the full outer shell that they're aiming for. And this means that they form ions with the **same charges**.

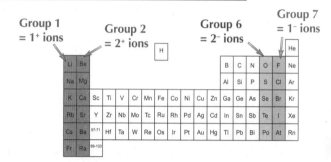

4) **Electrostatic attraction** holds positive and negative ions together — it's **very** strong. When atoms are held together like this, it's called **ionic bonding**.

> An **ionic bond** is an **electrostatic attraction** between two **oppositely charged** ions.

Not All Ions are Made from Single Atoms

There are lots of ions that are made up of a group of atoms with an overall charge. These are called **compound ions**. You need to remember the formulas of these ones:

Nitrate NO_3^-	**Carbonate** CO_3^{2-}	**Sulfate** SO_4^{2-}	**Ammonium** NH_4^+

Sodium Chloride and Magnesium Oxide are Ionic Compounds

1) The formula of sodium chloride is **NaCl**. It tells you that sodium chloride is made up of Na^+ and Cl^- **ions** in a 1:1 ratio.

2) You can use '**dot-and-cross**' diagrams to show how ionic bonding works in sodium chloride —

> Here, the dots represent the Na electrons and the crosses represent the Cl electrons (all electrons are really identical, but this is a good way of following their movement).

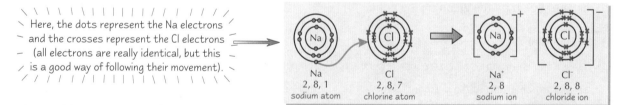

3) **Magnesium oxide**, MgO, is another good example:

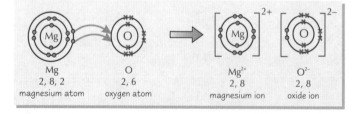

Dot (cross)

> The positive charges in the compound **balance** the negative charges exactly — so the total overall charge is **zero**. This is a dead handy way of checking the formula.
> - In **NaCl**, the single + charge on the Na^+ ion balances the single – charge on the Cl^- ion.
> - In $MgCl_2$ the 2+ charge on the Mg^{2+} ion balances the two – charges on the two Cl^- ions.

Ionic Bonding

Sodium Chloride has a *Giant Ionic Lattice* Structure

1) In **sodium chloride**, the Na^+ and Cl^- ions are packed together in a regular structure called a **lattice**.

2) The structure's called '**giant**' because it's made up of the same basic unit repeated over and over again.

3) The sodium chloride lattice is **cube** shaped — different ionic compounds have different shaped structures, but they're all still giant lattices.

4) Sodium chloride's got very strong **ionic bonds**, so it takes loads of **energy** to break up the lattice. This gives it a high melting point (801°C).

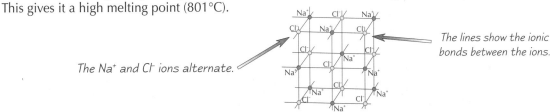

The Na⁺ and Cl⁻ ions alternate.

The lines show the ionic bonds between the ions.

But it's not just melting points — the structure decides other **physical properties** too...

Ionic Structure Explains the *Behaviour* of Ionic Compounds

1) **Ionic compounds conduct electricity when they're molten or dissolved — but not when they're solid.**
The ions in a liquid are free to move (and they carry a charge).
In a solid they're fixed in position by the strong ionic bonds.

2) **Ionic compounds have high melting points.**
The giant ionic lattices are held together by strong electrostatic forces. It takes loads of energy to overcome these forces, so melting points are very high (801 °C for sodium chloride).

3) **Ionic compounds tend to dissolve in water.**
Water molecules are polar — part of the molecule has a small negative charge, and the other bits have small positive charges (see p34). The water molecules pull the ions away from the lattice and cause it to dissolve.

Practice Questions

Q1 State the formula of the carbonate ion.

Q2 Draw a dot-and-cross diagram showing the bonding between magnesium and oxygen.

Q3 What type of force holds ionic substances together?

Q4 Why do many ionic compounds dissolve in water?

Exam Questions

Q1 a) Draw a labelled diagram to show the structure of sodium chloride. [3 marks]

b) What is the name of this type of structure? [1 mark]

c) Would you expect sodium chloride to have a high or a low melting point?
Explain your answer. [4 marks]

Q2 a) Ions can be formed by electron transfer. Explain this and give an example
of a positive and a negative ion. [3 marks]

b) Solid lead bromide does not conduct electricity, but molten lead bromide does.
Explain this with reference to ionic bonding. [4 marks]

A black fly in your Chardonnay — isn't it ionic...

This stuff's easy marks in exams. Just make sure you can draw dot-and-cross diagrams showing the bonding in ionic compounds, and you're sorted. Remember — atoms are lazy. It's easier to lose two electrons to get a full shell than it is to gain six, so that's what an atom's going to do. Practise drawing sodium chloride too, and don't stop till you're perfect.

Covalent Bonding

And now for covalent bonding — this is when atoms share electrons with one another so they've all got full outer shells.

Molecules *are Groups of Atoms* Bonded *Together*

Molecules are the **smallest parts** of compounds that can take part in chemical reactions.
They're formed when **2 or more** atoms bond together — it doesn't matter if the atoms are the **same** or **different**.
Chlorine gas (Cl_2), carbon monoxide (CO), water (H_2O) and ethanol (C_2H_5OH) are all molecules.

Molecules are held together by **covalent bonds**. In covalent bonding, two atoms **share** electrons, so they've **both** got full outer shells of electrons.

E.g. two hydrogen atoms bond covalently to form a molecule of hydrogen.

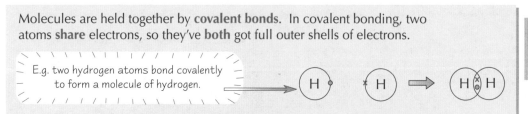

Covalent bonding happens between non-metals. Ionic bonding is between a metal and a non-metal.

A **covalent bond** is a **shared pair of electrons**.

Make sure you can Draw the Bonding in these Molecules

These diagrams don't show all the electrons in the molecules — just the ones in the **outer shells**:

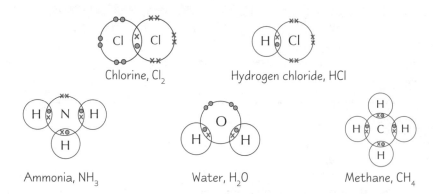

Chlorine, Cl_2

Hydrogen chloride, HCl

Ammonia, NH_3

Water, H_2O

Methane, CH_4

Most of the time the central atom ends up with **eight electrons** in its **outer shell**.
This is good for the atom — it's a very **stable** arrangement.

Hydrogen only needs to end up with 2 electrons to fill its outer shell.

Some Covalent Compounds Are Special Cases

There are always a few pesky exceptions to make life that bit trickier...

A few compounds have **less** than 8 electrons in their outer shell...

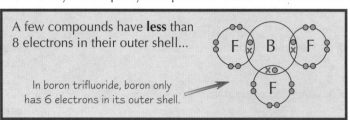

In boron trifluoride, boron only has 6 electrons in its outer shell.

And a few compounds can use d orbitals to **'expand the octet'**. This means they have more than 8 electrons in their outer shell.

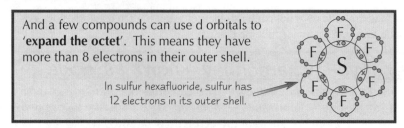

In sulfur hexafluoride, sulfur has 12 electrons in its outer shell.

Covalent Bonding

Some Atoms Share **More Than One Pair** of **Electrons**

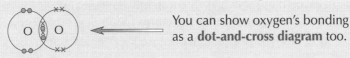

Atoms don't just form single bonds — some can form **double** or even **triple covalent bonds**. An example of a molecule that has a double bond is **oxygen**, O_2.

You can show oxygen's bonding as a **dot-and-cross diagram** too.

Nitrogen can triple bond, and carbon dioxide has two double bonds:

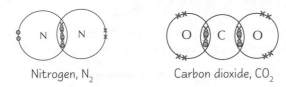

Nitrogen, N_2 Carbon dioxide, CO_2

Dative Covalent Bonding is where **Both Electrons** come from **One Atom**

The **ammonium ion** (NH_4^+) is formed by dative (or coordinate) covalent bonding — it's an example the examiners love. It forms when the nitrogen atom in an ammonia molecule **donates a pair of electrons** to a proton (H^+):

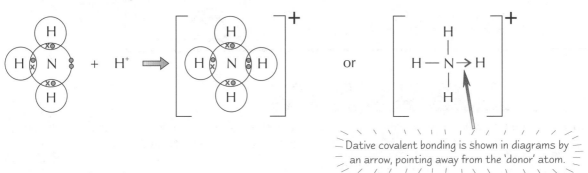

Dative covalent bonding is shown in diagrams by an arrow, pointing away from the 'donor' atom.

Practice Questions

Q1 Draw a dot-and-cross diagram to show the arrangement of the outer electrons in a molecule of hydrogen chloride.

Q2 What's special about the bonding in boron trifluoride?
Draw a diagram showing the outer electrons in a molecule of boron trifluoride.

Q3 Name a molecule with a double covalent bond. Draw a diagram showing the outer electrons in this molecule.

Exam Questions

Q1 Methane, CH_4, contains atoms of two non-metals.

a) What type of bonding would you expect it to have?   [1 mark]

b) Draw a dot-and-cross diagram to show the **full** electronic arrangement in a molecule of methane.   [2 marks]

Q2 a) What type of bonding is present in the ammonium ion (NH_4^+)?   [1 mark]

b) Explain how this type of bonding occurs.   [2 marks]

Interesting fact #795 — $TiCl_4$ is known as 'tickle' in the chemical industry...

More pretty diagrams to learn here folks — practise till you get every single dot and cross in the right place. It's totally amazing to think of these titchy little atoms sorting themselves out so they've got full outer shells of electrons. Remember — covalent bonding happens between two non-metals, whereas ionic bonding happens between a metal and a non-metal.

Giant Covalent Lattices and Metallic Bonding

Atoms can form giant structures as well as piddling little molecules — well... 'giant' in molecular terms anyway. Compared to structures like the Eiffel Tower or even your granny's carriage clock, they're still unbelievably tiny.

Diamond and Graphite are Giant Covalent Lattices

1) **Giant covalent lattices** are huge networks of **covalently** bonded atoms. (They're sometimes called **macromolecular structures** too.)

2) **Carbon** atoms can form this type of structure because they can each form four strong, covalent bonds.

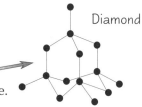
Diamond

Diamond is the Hardest known Substance

Diamond is made up of **carbon atoms**. Each carbon atom is **covalently bonded** to **four** other carbon atoms. The atoms arrange themselves in a **tetrahedral** shape — its crystal lattice structure.

Because of its **strong covalent** bonds:

1) Diamond has a **very high melting point** — it actually sublimes at over 3800 K.
2) Diamond is extremely **hard** — it's used in diamond-tipped drills and saws.
3) **Vibrations** travel easily through the stiff lattice, so it's a **good thermal conductor**.
4) It **can't conduct** electricity — all the outer electrons are held in localised bonds.
5) It won't dissolve in **any** solvent.

You can 'cut' diamond to form gemstones. Its structure makes it refract light a lot, which is why it sparkles.

'Sublimes' means it changes straight from a solid to a gas, skipping out the liquid stage.

Graphite is another Allotrope of Carbon

Allotropes are different forms of the **same element** in the **same state**. Carbon can form a number of different allotropes. Luckily, you only need to know about two of them — **diamond** and **graphite**.

The carbon atoms are arranged in sheets of flat hexagons covalently bonded with three bonds each.

The fourth outer electron of each carbon atom is delocalised between the sheets of hexagons.

Graphite

The sheets of hexagons are bonded together by weak van der Waals forces (see page 36).

Graphite's **structure** means it has some **different properties** from diamond.

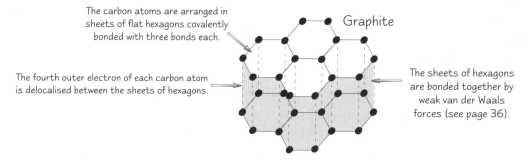

1) The weak bonds **between** the layers in graphite are easily broken, so the sheets can slide over each other — graphite feels **slippery** and is used as a **dry lubricant** and in **pencils**.
2) The 'delocalised' electrons in graphite aren't attached to any particular carbon atom and are **free to move** along the sheets, so an **electric current** can flow.
3) The layers are quite **far apart** compared to the length of the covalent bonds, so graphite is **less dense** than diamond and is used to make **strong, lightweight** sports equipment.
4) Because of the **strong covalent bonds** in the hexagon sheets, graphite also has a **very high melting point** (it sublimes at over 3900 K).
5) Like diamond, graphite is **insoluble** in any solvent. The covalent bonds in the sheets are **too difficult** to break.

Giant Covalent Lattices and Metallic Bonding

Metals have Giant Structures Too

Metal elements exist as **giant metallic lattice structures**.

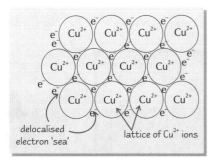

delocalised electron 'sea'

lattice of Cu^{2+} ions

1) The electrons in the outermost shell of a metal atom are **delocalised** — the electrons are free to move about the metal. This leaves a **positive metal ion**, e.g. Na^+, Mg^{2+}, Al^{3+}.

2) The positive metal ions are **attracted** to the delocalised negative electrons. They form a lattice of closely packed positive ions in a **sea** of delocalised electrons — this is **metallic bonding**.

Metallic bonding explains why metals do what they do —

1) The **number of delocalised electrons per atom** affects the melting point. The **more** there are, the **stronger** the bonding will be and the **higher** the melting point. Mg^{2+} has **two** delocalised electrons per atom, so it's got a **higher melting point** than Na^+, which only has **one**. The **size** of the metal ion and the **lattice structure** also affect the melting point.

2) As there are **no bonds** holding specific ions together, the metal ions can slide past each other when the structure is pulled, so metals are **malleable** (can be hammered into sheets) and **ductile** (can be drawn into a wire).

3) The delocalised electrons can pass **kinetic energy** to each other, making metals **good thermal conductors**.

4) Metals are **good electrical conductors** because the **delocalised electrons** can carry a **current**.

5) Metals are **insoluble**, except in **liquid metals**, because of the **strength** of the metallic bonds.

Practice Questions

Q1 How are the carbon sheets in graphite held together?

Q2 Diamond has a giant covalent lattice structure. Give two properties that it has as a result of this.

Q3 Why are metals malleable?

Exam Questions

Q1 Carbon can be found as the allotropes diamond and graphite.
   a) What type of structure do diamond and graphite display? [1 mark]

   b) Draw diagrams to illustrate the structures of diamond and graphite. [2 marks]

   c) Compare and explain the electrical conductivities of diamond and graphite in terms of their structure and bonding. [4 marks]

Q2 Illustrate with a suitable labelled diagram the structure of copper and explain what is meant by metallic bonding. [4 marks]

Carbon is a girl's best friend...

Examiners love giving you questions on diamond and graphite. Close the book and do a quick sketch of each allotrope, together with a list of their properties — then look back at the page and see what you missed. It might be less fun than ironing your underwear, but it's much more useful and the only way to make sure you sparkle in the exam.

Shapes of Molecules

Chemistry would be heaps more simple if all molecules were flat. But they're not.

Molecular Shape depends on Electron Pairs around the Central Atom

Molecules and molecular ions come in loads of **different shapes**.
The shape depends on the **number of pairs** of electrons in the outer shell of the central atom.

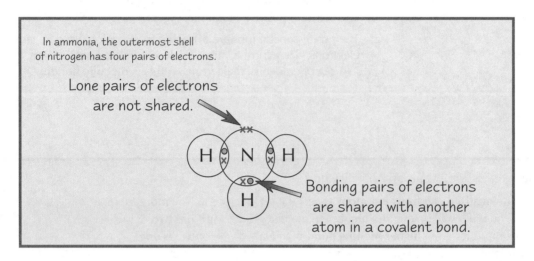

In ammonia, the outermost shell
of nitrogen has four pairs of electrons.

Lone pairs of electrons
are not shared.

Bonding pairs of electrons
are shared with another
atom in a covalent bond.

A lone pear

Electron Pairs Repel Each Other

1) Electrons are all **negatively charged**, so it's pretty obvious that
   electron pairs will **repel** each other as much as they can.

2) This sounds straightforward, but the **type** of the electron pair affects **how much** it repels other electron pairs.
   Lone pairs repel **more** than bonding pairs.

3) So, the **greatest** angles are between **lone pairs** of electrons, and bond angles between
   bonding pairs are often **reduced** because they are pushed together by lone-pair repulsion.

Lone-pair/lone-pair bond angles are the biggest.	*Lone-pair/bonding-pair bond angles are the second biggest.*	*Bonding-pair/bonding-pair bond angles are the smallest.*

4) This is known by the long-winded name '**Valence-Shell Electron-Pair Repulsion Theory**'.

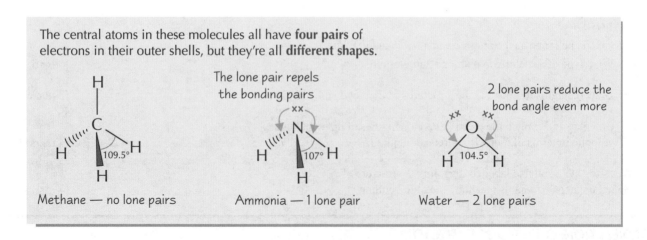

The central atoms in these molecules all have **four pairs** of
electrons in their outer shells, but they're all **different shapes**.

The lone pair repels
the bonding pairs

2 lone pairs reduce the
bond angle even more

Methane — no lone pairs   Ammonia — 1 lone pair   Water — 2 lone pairs

Shapes of Molecules

Practise **Drawing** these Molecules

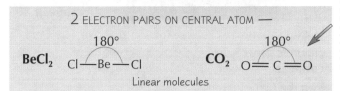

2 ELECTRON PAIRS ON CENTRAL ATOM —

Just treat double bonds the same as single bonds (even though there might be slightly more repulsion from a double bond).

BeCl$_2$ Cl—Be—Cl   180°

CO$_2$ O=C=O   180°

Linear molecules

3 ELECTRON PAIRS ON CENTRAL ATOM —

BF$_3$ 120°

AlCl$_3$ 120°

no lone pairs — trigonal planar

4 ELECTRON PAIRS ON CENTRAL ATOM —

NH$_4^+$ 109.5°
no lone pairs — tetrahedral

NH$_3$ 107°

SO$_3^{2-}$ 107°
1 lone pair — trigonal pyramidal

H$_2$O   104.5°
2 lone pairs — non-linear or "bent"

6 ELECTRON PAIRS ON CENTRAL ATOM —

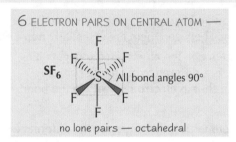

SF$_6$ All bond angles 90°

no lone pairs — octahedral

Practice Questions

Q1 What is a lone pair of electrons?

Q2 Explain why a water molecule is not linear.

Q3 Write down the order of the strength of repulsion between different kinds of electron pair.

Q4 Draw a tetrahedral molecule.

Exam Question

Q1 Nitrogen and boron can form the chlorides NCl_3 and BCl_3.

a) Draw 'dot and cross' diagrams to show the bonding in NCl_3 and BCl_3.   [2 marks]

b) Draw the shapes of the molecules NCl_3 and BCl_3.
Show the approximate values of the bond angles on the diagrams and name each shape.   [6 marks]

c) Explain why the shapes of NCl_3 and BCl_3 are different.   [3 marks]

These molecules ain't square...

In the exam, those evil examiners might try to throw you by asking you to predict the shape of an unfamiliar molecule. Don't panic — it'll be just like one you do know, e.g. PH$_3$ is the same shape as NH$_3$. Make sure you can draw every single molecule on this page. Yep, that's right — from memory. And you need to know what the shapes are called too.

Electronegativity and Intermolecular Forces

Intermolecular forces hold molecules together. They're pretty important, cos we'd all be gassy clouds without them.

There's a Gradual **Transition** from Ionic to Covalent Bonding

1) Very few compounds come even close to being **purely ionic**.

2) Only bonds between atoms of a **single** element, like diatomic gases such as hydrogen (H_2) or oxygen (O_2), can be **purely covalent**.

3) So really, most compounds come somewhere **in between** the two extremes — meaning they've often got ionic **and** covalent properties, e.g. covalent hydrogen chloride gas molecules dissolve to form hydrochloric acid, which is an ionic solution. $HCl_{(g)} \xrightarrow{H_2O} H^+_{(aq)} + Cl^-_{(aq)}$

Covalent Bonds may be Polarised by **Differences** in **Electronegativity**

The ability to attract the bonding electrons in a covalent bond is called **electronegativity**. **Fluorine** is the most electronegative element. **Oxygen**, **nitrogen** and **chlorine** are also very strongly electronegative.

Electronegativity increases across periods and decreases down groups (ignoring the noble gases).

1) In a covalent bond between two atoms of **different** electronegativities, the bonding electrons are **pulled towards** the more electronegative atom. This makes the bond **polar**.

2) The covalent bonds in diatomic gases (e.g. H_2, Cl_2) are **non-polar** because the atoms have **equal** electronegativities and so the electrons are equally attracted to both nuclei.

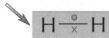

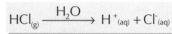

Permanent polar bonding

3) Some elements, like carbon and hydrogen, have pretty **similar** electronegativities, so bonds between them are essentially **non-polar**.

4) In a **polar bond**, the difference in the atoms' electronegativities causes a **dipole**. A dipole is a **difference in charge** between the two atoms caused by a shift in **electron density** in the bond.

'δ' (delta) means 'slightly', so 'δ+' means 'slightly positive'.

5) So what you need to **remember** is that the greater the **difference** in electronegativity, the **more polar** the bond.

Polar Molecules Mean Intermolecular Attraction

Intermolecular forces are forces between molecules. They're much weaker than covalent, ionic or metallic bonds.

The δ+ and δ- charges on **polar molecules** cause **weak electrostatic forces** of attraction **between** molecules. These are called **permanent dipole-dipole interactions**.

E.g. hydrogen chloride gas has polar molecules.

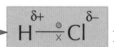

Now this is pretty cool:
If you put an **electrostatically charged rod** next to a polar liquid, like water, the liquid will **move** towards the rod. I wouldn't believe me either, but it's true. It's because **polar liquids** contain molecules with **permanent dipoles**. It doesn't matter if the rod is **positively** or **negatively** charged. The polar molecules in the liquid can **turn around** so the oppositely charged end is attracted towards the rod.

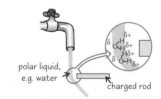

polar liquid, e.g. water

charged rod

Intermolecular Forces are **Very Weak**

There are three types of **intermolecular force** you need to know about, but they're all very **weak** compared to the bonds **within** the molecule.

Sometimes the term 'van der Waals forces' is considered to include all three types of intermolecular force.

1) **Permanent dipole-dipole interactions** (see previous page)
2) **Hydrogen bonding** (this is the strongest type)
3) **Temporary dipole-induced dipole** or **van der Waals** forces — this is the weakest type

See page 36 for more info.

Electronegativity and Intermolecular Forces

Hydrogen Bonding is the Strongest Intermolecular Force

1) Hydrogen bonding can **only** happen when **hydrogen** is covalently bonded to **fluorine**, **nitrogen** or **oxygen**. Hydrogen has a **high charge density** because it's so small and fluorine, nitrogen and oxygen are very **electronegative**. The bond is so **polarised** that the hydrogen of one molecule forms a weak bond with the fluorine, nitrogen or oxygen of **another molecule**.

2) Molecules which have hydrogen bonding are usually **organic**, containing **-OH** or **-NH** groups.

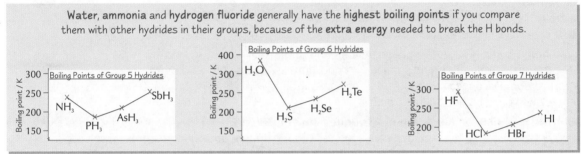

Water and ammonia both have hydrogen bonding.

A lone pair of electrons on the oxygen is attracted to the hydrogen.

3) Hydrogen bonding has a huge effect on the properties of substances. They are **soluble** in water and have **higher boiling and freezing points** than non-polar molecules of a similar size.

Water, ammonia and hydrogen fluoride generally have the **highest boiling points** if you compare them with other hydrides in their groups, because of the **extra energy** needed to break the H bonds.

Boiling Points of Group 5 Hydrides

Boiling Points of Group 6 Hydrides

Boiling Points of Group 7 Hydrides

4) In ice, molecules of H_2O are held together in a **lattice** by hydrogen bonds. And because hydrogen bonds are relatively **long**, ice is **less dense** than liquid water. ← This is unusual... most substances get denser when they freeze.

Practice Questions

Q1 What are the only bonds which can be purely covalent?

Q2 What is the most electronegative element?

Q3 What is a dipole?

Q4 What atoms must be covalently bonded together for hydrogen bonding to exist?

Exam Questions

Q1 Many covalent molecules have a permanent dipole, due to differences in electronegativities.

    a) Define the term electronegativity. [2 marks]

    b) Draw the shapes and marking any bond polarities clearly on your diagram: (i) Br_2 (ii) H_2O (iii) NH_3 [5 marks]

Q2 a) Name three types of intermolecular force. [3 marks]

    b) Water, H_2O, boils at 373 K.

        (i) Explain why water's boiling point is higher than expected in comparison to other similar molecules. [2 marks]

        (ii) Draw a labelled diagram showing the intermolecular bonding that takes place in water. [2 marks]

Enough of this chemistry rubbish. Here are some interesting facts...

If you chop the head off a beetle, it wouldn't die of being beheaded, but actually starvation. It's true. If you ate 14 lbs of almonds, you'd die of cyanide poisoning. It's true! Daddy-long-legs are actually the most poisonous insects in the world, but they can't pierce the skin... it's TRUE. Every night, the human body sweats enough to fill a swimming pool. It's true...

Van der Waals Forces

Hang on in there — you're almost at the end of the section. If you can just hold out for another two pages...

Van der Waals Forces are Found Between **All** Atoms and Molecules

Van der Waals forces cause **all** atoms and molecules to be **attracted** to each other.
Even **noble gas atoms** are affected, despite not being at all interested in forming other types of bond.

1) **Electrons** in charge clouds are always **moving** really quickly.
At any particular moment, the electrons in an atom are likely
to be more to one side than the other. At this moment, the
atom would have a **temporary dipole**.

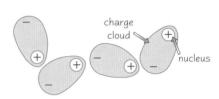

charge cloud

nucleus

2) This dipole can cause **another** temporary dipole in the opposite direction on
a neighbouring atom. The two dipoles are then **attracted** to each other.

3) The second dipole can cause yet another dipole in a **third atom**. It's kind of like a domino rally.

4) Because the electrons are constantly moving, the dipoles are being **created** and **destroyed** all the time.
Even though the dipoles keep changing, the **overall effect** is for the atoms to be **attracted** to each other.

Stronger **Van der Waals Forces** mean **Higher Boiling Points**

1) Not all van der Waals forces are the same strength —
larger molecules have **larger electron clouds**, meaning
stronger van der Waals forces. Molecules with greater
surface areas also have stronger van der Waals forces
because they have a **bigger exposed electron cloud**.

Van der Waals forces affect other physical properties, such as melting point and viscosity, too.

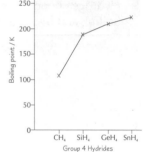

Boiling Points of Group 4 Hydrides

Boiling point / K

CH_4 SiH_4 GeH_4 SnH_4
Group 4 Hydrides

2) When you **boil** a liquid, you need to **overcome** the intermolecular forces, so that the
particles can **escape** from the liquid surface. It stands to reason that you need **more
energy** to overcome **stronger** intermolecular forces, so liquids with stronger van der
Waals forces will have **higher boiling points**.

3) This graph of the boiling points of Group 4 hydrides shows the trend.
As you go down the group, the van der Waals forces (and the boiling points) increase because:
(i) the **atomic/molecular size** increases, (ii) the number of **shells** of electrons increases.

Van der Waals Forces Can Hold Molecules in a **Lattice**

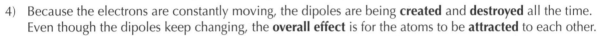

Van der Waals forces are responsible for holding **iodine** molecules together in a **lattice**.

1) Iodine atoms are held together in pairs by **strong** covalent bonds to form
molecules of I_2.

2) But the molecules are then held together
in a **molecular lattice** arrangement by
weak van der Waals attractions.

Covalent Bonds **Don't** Break during **Melting** and **Boiling**

Except for giant molecular substances, like diamond.

This is something that confuses loads of people — get it sorted in **your** head now...

1) To **melt** or **boil** a simple covalent compound you only have to overcome the
van der Waals forces or **hydrogen bonds** that hold the molecules together.

When you boil water, you don't get hydrogen and oxygen.

2) You **don't** need to break the much stronger covalent bonds that hold
the atoms together in the molecules.

3) That's why simple covalent compounds have relatively **low melting** and **boiling points**.

For example: Chlorine, Cl_2, has stronger covalent bonds than bromine, Br_2.
But under normal conditions, chlorine is a gas and bromine a liquid.
Bromine has the higher boiling point because its molecules are bigger,
giving stronger van der Waals forces.

Van der Waals Forces

Learn the **Properties** of the Main Substance Types

Nearly finished... but not quite. Before you mentally clock off, make sure you know how all the various types of attraction between atoms and molecules affect a substance's **properties**. You need to know this table like the back of your spam...

Bonding	Examples	Melting and boiling points	Typical state at STP	Does solid conduct electricity?	Does liquid conduct electricity?	Is it soluble in water?
Ionic	NaCl MgCl$_2$	High	Solid	No (ions are held firmly in place)	Yes (ions are free to move)	Yes
Simple molecular (covalent)	CO$_2$ I$_2$ H$_2$O	Low (have to overcome van der Waals forces or hydrogen bonds, not covalent bonds)	Sometimes solid, usually liquid or gas (water is liquid because it has hydrogen bonds)	No	No	Depends on how polarised the molecule is
Giant covalent lattice	Diamond Graphite	High	Solid	No (except graphite)	— (will generally sublime)	No
Metallic	Fe Mg Al	High	Solid	Yes (delocalised electrons)	Yes (delocalised electrons)	No

Practice Questions

Q1 Explain why van der Waals attractions are present even in neutral atoms like argon.

Q2 Describe some of the effects of van der Waals forces on the physical properties of substances.

Q3 Describe two factors that affect the size of van der Waals forces.

Q4 What types of bond must be overcome in order for a simple molecular substance to boil or melt?

Q5 Do ionic compounds conduct electricity?

Q6 Why can metals conduct electricity?

Exam Questions

Q1

Substance	Melting point	Electrical conductivity of solid	Electrical conductivity of liquid	Solubility in water
A	High	Poor	Good	Soluble
B	Low	Poor	Poor	Insoluble
C	High	Good	Good	Insoluble
D	Very High	Poor	Poor	Insoluble

a) Identify the type of crystal structure present in each substance, A to D. [4 marks]

b) Which substance is most likely to be:
   (i) diamond, (ii) aluminium, (iii) sodium chloride and (iv) iodine? [2 marks]

Q2 Explain the electrical conductivity of magnesium, sodium chloride and graphite.
In your answer you should consider the structure and bonding of each of these materials. [12 marks]

Van der Waal — a Dutch hit for Oasis...

You need to learn the info in the table above. With a quick glance in my crystal ball, I can almost guarantee you'll need a bit of it in your exam... let me look a bit closer and tell you which bit... mmm.... Nah — it's clouded over... you'll have to learn the lot. Sorry. Tell you what — close the book and see how much of the table you can scribble out from memory.

The Periodic Table

As far as Chemistry topics go, the Periodic Table is a bit of a biggie. So much so that they even want you to know the history of it. So make yourself comfortable and I'll tell you a story that began... oh, about 200 years ago...

In the **1800s**, Elements Could Only Be Grouped by **Atomic Mass**

1) In the early 1800s, there were only two ways to categorise elements — by their **physical and chemical properties** and by their **relative atomic mass**. (The modern periodic table is arranged by **proton number**, but back then, they knew nothing about protons or electrons. The only thing they could measure was relative atomic mass.)

2) In 1817, Johann Döbereiner attempted to group similar elements — these groups were called **Döbereiner's triads**. He saw that **chlorine**, **bromine** and **iodine** had similar characteristics. He also realised that other properties of bromine (e.g. atomic weight) fell **halfway** between those of chlorine and iodine. He found other such groups of three elements (e.g. lithium, sodium and potassium), and called them **triads**. It was a start.

3) An English chemist called **John Newlands** had the first good stab at making a table of the elements in 1863. He noticed that if he arranged the elements in order of **mass**, similar elements appeared at regular intervals — every **eighth element** was similar. He called this the **law of octaves**, and he listed some known elements in rows of seven so that the similar elements lined up in columns.

Li	Be	B	C	N	O	F
Na	Mg	Al	Si	P	S	Cl

4) The problem was, the pattern broke down on the third row, with many transition metals like Fe, Cu and Zn messing it up completely.

Dmitri Mendeleev Created the **First Accepted Version**

1) In 1869, Russian chemist **Dmitri Mendeleev** produced a much better table, which wasn't far off the one we have today.

2) He arranged all the known elements by atomic mass (like Newlands did), but the clever thing he did was to leave **gaps** in the table where the next element didn't seem to fit. By putting in gaps, he could keep elements with similar chemical properties in the same group.

3) He also predicted the properties of **undiscovered elements** that would go in the gaps.

4) When elements were **later discovered** (e.g. germanium, scandium and gallium) with properties that matched Mendeleev's predictions, it showed that clever old Mendeleev had got it right.

	Group 1	Group 2	Gr
Period 1	H		
Period 2	Li	Be	
Period 3	Na	Mg	
Period 4	K Cu	Ca Zn	*
Period 5	Rb Ag	Sr Cd	Y

What do you think of the table? I made it myself...   Oh, Dmitri, I love it...

The **Modern Periodic Table** Arranges Elements by **Proton Number**

The modern Periodic Table is pretty much the one produced by Henry Moseley in 1914.

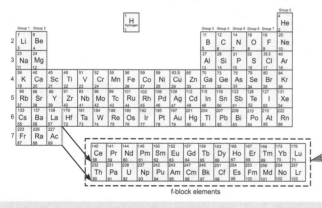

f-block elements

1) He arranged the elements according to **atomic number** rather than by mass.

2) This fixed a few elements that Mendeleev had put out of place using atomic mass.

3) He also added the **noble gases** (Group 0) which had been discovered in the 1890s.

4) The final big change was a result of the work of **Glenn Seaborg**. He suggested how the **f-block** elements fit into the Periodic Table (though they're usually shown separated from the main part of the table).

1) The modern Periodic Table is arranged into **periods** (rows) and **groups** (columns).

2) All the elements **within a period** have the same number of **electron shells** (if you don't worry about the sub-shells)
   — the elements of Period 1 (hydrogen and helium) both have 1 electron shell.
   — the elements in Period 2 have 2 electron shells. And so on down the table...

3) All the elements **within a group** have the same number of **electrons in their outer shell**. This means they have similar physical and chemical properties. The group number tells you the number of electrons in the outer shell, e.g. Group 1 elements have 1 electron in their outer shell, Group 4 elements have 4 electrons, and so on...

The Periodic Table

You can use the Periodic Table to work out *Electron Configurations*

The Periodic Table can be split into an **s block**, **d block** and **p block** like this:
Doing this shows you which sub-shells all the electrons go into.

See page 22 if this sub-shell malarkey doesn't ring a bell.

| s block |
| d block |
| p block |

1) The **s-block** elements have an outer shell electron configuration of s^1 or s^2.

   Examples Lithium ($1s^2\ 2s^1$) and magnesium ($1s^2\ 2s^2\ 2p^6\ 3s^2$)

2) The **p-block** elements have an outer shell configuration of s^2p^1 to s^2p^6.

   Example Chlorine ($1s^2\ 2s^2\ 2p^6\ 3s^2\ 3p^5$)

3) The **d-block** elements have electron configurations in which d sub-shells are being filled.

   Example Cobalt ($1s^2\ 2s^2\ 2p^6\ 3s^2\ 3p^6\ 3d^7\ 4s^2$)

   Even though the 3d sub-shell fills last in cobalt, it's not written at the end of the line.

When you've got the Periodic Table **labelled** with the **shells** and **sub-shells** like the one up there, it's pretty easy to read off the electron structure of any element by starting at the top and working your way across and down until you get to your element.

Example

Electron structure of phosphorus (P):
Period 1 — $1s^2$ ⟵ Complete sub-shells
Period 2 — $2s^2\ 2p^6$ ⟵
Period 3 — $3s^2\ 3p^3$ ⟵ Incomplete outer sub-shell

A wee apology...
This bit's really hard to explain clearly in words. If you're confused, just look at the examples until you get it...

Practice Questions

Q1 In what ways is Newlands' 'periodic table' not as good as Mendeleev's?

Q2 In what order did Mendeleev originally set out the elements?

Q3 In what order are the elements set out in the modern Periodic Table? Who was the first to do this?

Q4 What is the name given to the columns in the Periodic Table?

Q5 What is the name given to the rows in the Periodic Table? *(Err, hello — easy questions alert.)*

Exam Question

Q1 a) Complete the electronic configuration of sodium: $1s^2$ _____

   b) State the block in the Periodic Table to which sodium belongs.

   c) Complete the electronic configuration of bromine: $1s^2$ _____

   d) State the block in the Periodic Table to which bromine belongs. [4 marks]

<u>Periodic — probably the best table in the world...*</u>

Dropped History for AS Chemistry, did you... Ha, bet you're regretting that now, aren't you. If so, you'll enjoy the free History lesson that you get here with the Periodic Table. Make sure you learn all the key details and particularly how to spell Mendeleev. This stuff's not here for fun — it's here because you're gonna get questions on it.

*Excluding Dinner and the Round, of course.

Periodic Trends

Periodicity is one of those words you hear a lot in Chemistry without ever really knowing what it means. Well it basically means the trends that occur (in physical and chemical properties) as you move across the periods. E.g. Metal to non-metal is a trend that occurs going left to right in each period...

Atomic Radius **Decreases** across a Period

1) As the number of protons increases, the **positive charge** of the nucleus increases. This means electrons are **pulled closer** to the nucleus, making the atomic radius smaller.

2) The extra electrons that the elements gain across a period are added to the **outer energy level** so they don't really provide any extra shielding effect (shielding works with inner shells mainly).

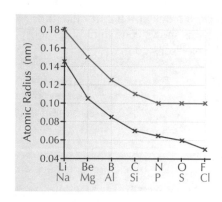

Ionisation Energy **Increases** across a Period...

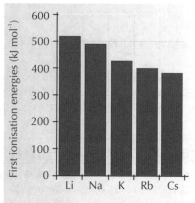

See page 24 for more on ionisation energies.

Don't forget — there are **3 main things** that affect the size of ionisation energies:

1) **Atomic radius** — the further the outer shell electrons from the nucleus, the lower the ionisation energy.

2) **Nuclear charge** — the **more protons** in the nucleus, the higher the ionisation energy.

3) **Electron shielding** — the more inner shells there are, the more shielding there is, and the lower the ionisation energy.

The graph below shows the first ionisation energies of the elements in **Periods 2 and 3**.

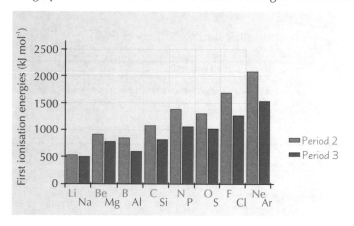

1) As you **move across** a period, the **general trend** is for the ionisation energies to **increase** — i.e. it gets harder to remove the outer electrons.

2) This is because the number of protons is increasing, which means a stronger **nuclear attraction**.

3) All the extra electrons are at **roughly the same** energy level, even if the outer electrons are in different orbital types.

4) This means there's generally little **extra shielding** effect or **extra distance** to lessen the attraction from the nucleus.

...and **Decreases** Down a Group

As you **go down** a group in the Periodic Table, ionisation energies generally **fall**, i.e. it gets **easier** to remove outer electrons. This is because:

- Elements further down a group have **extra electron shells** compared to ones above. The extra shells mean that the outer electrons are **further away** from the nucleus, which greatly reduces the attraction to the nucleus.

- The extra inner shells **shield** the outer electrons from the attraction of the nucleus.

First ionisation energies of the first five elements of Group 1.

The positive charge of the nucleus does increase as you go down a group (due to the extra protons), but this effect is overridden by the effect of the extra shells.

Periodic Trends

Melting and Boiling Points are linked to **Bond Strength** and **Structure**

Periods 2 and 3 show similar trends in their melting and boiling points. These trends are linked to changes in **structure** and **bond strength**.

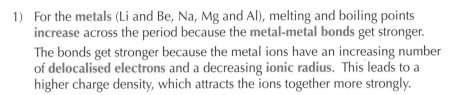

1) For the **metals** (Li and Be, Na, Mg and Al), melting and boiling points **increase** across the period because the **metal-metal bonds** get stronger.

   The bonds get stronger because the metal ions have an increasing number of **delocalised electrons** and a decreasing **ionic radius**. This leads to a higher charge density, which attracts the ions together more strongly.

2) The elements with **macromolecular** structures have **strong covalent bonds** linking all their atoms together. **A lot** of energy is needed to break these bonds. So, for example, carbon (as graphite or diamond) and silicon have the **highest** melting and boiling points in their periods. (The carbon data in the graph opposite is for graphite — diamond has an even higher boiling point. But neither of them actually melts or boils at atmospheric pressure, they sublime from solid to gas.)

3) Next come the **simple molecular substances** (N_2, O_2 and F_2, P_4, S_8 and Cl_2). Their melting and boiling points depend upon the strength of the **van der Waals forces** (see p36) between their molecules. Van der Waals forces are weak and easily overcome so these elements have **low** melting and boiling points.

4) More atoms in a molecule mean stronger van der Waals forces. For example, in Period 3 sulfur is the **biggest molecule** (S_8), so it's got higher melting and boiling points than phosphorus or chlorine.

5) The noble gases (neon and argon) have the **lowest** melting and boiling points because they exist as **individual atoms** (they're monatomic) resulting in **very weak** van der Waals forces.

Practice Questions

Q1 Name three factors that affect the size of ionisation energies.

Q2 How does the first ionisation energy change as you go across a period?

Q3 Which element in Period 3 has the highest melting point? Which has the highest boiling point?

Q4 Why does phosphorus have a lower melting point than magnesium?

Exam Questions

Q1 Explain why first ionisation energies show an overall tendency to increase across a period. [3 marks]

Q2 Explain why the melting point of magnesium is higher than that of sodium. [3 marks]

Q3 This table shows the melting points for the Period 3 elements.

Element	Na	Mg	Al	Si	P	S	Cl	Ar
Melting point / K	371	923	933	1680	317	392	172	84

In terms of structure and bonding explain why:

a) silicon has a high melting point. [2 marks]

b) the melting point of sulfur is higher than that of phosphorus. [2 marks]

Q4 State and explain the trend in atomic radius across Period 3. [4 marks]

Periodic trends — my mate Dom's always a decade behind...

He still thinks Oasis, Blur and REM are the best bands around. The sad muppet. But not me. Oh no sirree, I'm up with the times — April Lavigne... Linkin' Pork... Christina Agorrilla. I'm hip, I'm with it. Da ga da ga da ga da ga... _ooaarrr ooup *_   * _Obscure reference to Austin Powers: International Man of Mystery. You should watch it — it's better than doing Chemistry._

Group 2 — The Alkaline Earth Metals

It would be easy for Group 2 elements to feel slightly inferior to those in Group 1. They're only in the second group, after all. That's why you should try to get to know and like them. They'd really appreciate it, I'm sure.

Group 2 Elements Form 2+ Ions

Element	Atom	Ion
Be	$1s^2\,2s^2$	$1s^2$
Mg	$1s^2\,2s^2\,2p^6\,3s^2$	$1s^2\,2s^2\,2p^6$
Ca	$1s^2\,2s^2\,2p^6\,3s^2\,3p^6\,4s^2$	$1s^2\,2s^2\,2p^6\,3s^2\,3p^6$

Group 2 elements all have two electrons in their outer shell (s^2).

They lose their two outer electrons to form **2+ ions**. Their ions then have every atom's dream electronic structure — that of a **noble gas**.

Reactivity **Increases** Down Group 2

1) As you go down the group, the **ionisation energies** decrease. This is due to the **increasing atomic radius** and **shielding effect** (see p40).

2) When Group 2 elements react they **lose electrons**, forming positive ions (**cations**). The easier it is to lose electrons (i.e. the lower the first and second ionisation energies), the more reactive the element, so **reactivity increases** down the group.

Mr Kelly has one final attempt at explaining electron shielding to his students...

Group 2 Elements React with **Water** and **Oxygen**

When Group 2 elements react, they are **oxidised** from a state of **0** to **+2**, forming M^{2+} ions. This is because Group 2 atoms contain 2 electrons in their outer shell.

$$M \rightarrow M^{2+} + 2e^- \qquad \text{E.g. } Ca \rightarrow Ca^{2+} + 2e^-$$
Oxidation number: 0 +2   0   +2

1) GROUP 2 ELEMENTS REACT WITH WATER TO PRODUCE HYDROXIDES

The Group 2 metals react with water to give a **metal hydroxide and hydrogen**.

$$M_{(s)} + 2H_2O_{(l)} \rightarrow M(OH)_{2\,(aq)} + H_{2\,(g)}$$
Oxidation number: 0   +2

e.g.

$$Ca_{(s)} + 2H_2O_{(l)} \rightarrow Ca(OH)_{2\,(aq)} + H_{2\,(g)}$$

Be	doesn't react
Mg	VERY slowly
Ca	steadily
Sr	fairly quickly
Ba	rapidly

These are redox reactions — see p20 for more info.

2) THEY BURN IN OXYGEN TO FORM OXIDES

When Group 2 metals burn in oxygen, you get solid white **oxides**.

$$2M_{(s)} + O_{2\,(g)} \rightarrow 2MO_{(s)}$$
Oxidation number of metal: 0   +2
Oxidation number of oxygen: 0   −2

e.g.

$$2Ca_{(s)} + O_{2\,(g)} \rightarrow 2CaO_{(s)}$$
0   +2
0   −2

Group 2 Oxides and Hydroxides are **Bases**

THEY FORM ALKALINE SOLUTIONS IN WATER...

1) The **oxides** of the Group 2 metals react readily with **water** to form **metal hydroxides**, which dissolve. The **hydroxide ions, OH⁻**, make these solutions **strongly alkaline** (e.g. pH 12 - 13).

2) Magnesium oxide is an exception — it only reacts slowly and the hydroxide isn't very soluble.

$$CaO_{(s)} + H_2O_{(l)} \rightarrow Ca^{2+}_{(aq)} + 2OH^-_{(aq)}$$

3) The oxides form **more strongly alkaline** solutions as you go down the group, because the hydroxides get more soluble.

Group 2 — The Alkaline Earth Metals

Thermal Stability of Carbonates Changes Down the Group

Thermal decomposition is when a substance **breaks down** (decomposes) when **heated**. The more thermally stable a substance is, the more heat it will take to break it down. Here's how it goes for **Group 2 carbonates...**

1) **Group 2 carbonates decompose to form the oxide and carbon dioxide.**

$$MCO_{3\,(s)} \quad \rightarrow \quad MO_{(s)} + CO_{2\,(g)}$$
$$\text{e.g.} \quad CaCO_{3\,(s)} \quad \rightarrow \quad CaO_{(s)} + CO_{2\,(g)}$$

2) **Thermal stability increases down the group.**
   So, it's take **more heat** to decompose, say, calcium carbonate than magnesium carbonate.

Group 2 Compounds are used to Neutralise Acidity

Group 2 elements are known as the **alkaline earth metals**, and many of their common compounds are used for neutralising acids. Here are a couple of common examples:

1) Calcium hydroxide (slaked lime, $Ca(OH)_2$) is used in **agriculture** to neutralise acid soils.

Daisy the cow *

2) Magnesium hydroxide ($Mg(OH)_2$) is used in some indigestion tablets as an **antacid**.

In both cases, the ionic equation for the neutralisation is
$$H^+_{(aq)} + OH^-_{(aq)} \rightarrow H_2O_{(l)}$$

*She wanted to be in the book. I said OK.

Practice Questions

Q1 Which is the least reactive metal in Group 2?

Q2 Why does reactivity with water increase down Group 2?

Q3 Which of the following increases in size down Group 2? **atomic radius, first ionisation energy**

Q4 Give a use of magnesium hydroxide.

Q5 Write an equation for the thermal decomposition of calcium carbonate.

Exam Questions

Q1 The reactivity of an element depends on its ionisation energies. Explain the difference in first ionisation energies of magnesium and calcium. [4 marks]

Q2 Calcium (Ca) can be burned in oxygen.
   a) Write an equation for the reaction. [1 mark]
   b) Show the change in oxidation state of calcium. [1 mark]
   c) Predict the appearance of the product. [2 marks]
   d) What type of bonding does the product have? [1 mark]

Q3 The table shows the atomic radii of three elements from Group 2.

Element	Atomic radius (nm)
X	0.089
Y	0.198
Z	0.176

   a) Predict which element would react most rapidly with water. [1 mark]
   b) Explain your answer. [2 marks]

I'm not gonna make it. You've gotta get me out of here, Doc...

We're deep in the dense jungle of Inorganic Chemistry now. Those carefree days of Section Two are well behind us. It's now an endurance test and you've just got to keep going. By now, all the facts are probably blurring into one. It's tough, but you've got to stay awake, stay focused and keep learning. That's all you can do.

Group 7 — The Halogens

Now you can wave goodbye to those pesky s-block elements. Here come the halogens.

Halogens are the **Highly Reactive Non-Metals** of Group 7

The table below gives some of the main properties of the first 4 halogens.

halogen	formula	colour	physical state	electronic structure
fluorine	F_2	pale yellow	gas	$1s^2\ 2s^2\ 2p^5$
chlorine	Cl_2	green	gas	$1s^2\ 2s^2\ 2p^6\ 3s^2\ 3p^5$
bromine	Br_2	red-brown	liquid	$1s^2\ 2s^2\ 2p^6\ 3s^2\ 3p^6\ 3d^{10}\ 4s^2\ 4p^5$
iodine	I_2	grey	solid	$1s^2\ 2s^2\ 2p^6\ 3s^2\ 3p^6\ 3d^{10}\ 4s^2\ 4p^6\ 4d^{10}\ 5s^2\ 5p^5$

The boiling and melting points of the halogens increase down the group. This is due to the increasing strength of the **van der Waals forces** as the size and relative mass of the atoms increases. This trend is shown in the changes of **physical state** from chlorine (gas) to iodine (solid). (A substance is said to be **volatile** if it has a low boiling point. So volatility **decreases** down the group.)

The word <u>halogen</u> should be used when describing the atom (X) or molecule (X_2), but the word <u>halide</u> is used to describe the negative ion (X^-).

Halogens get **Less Reactive** Down the Group

1) Halogen atoms react by **gaining an electron** in their outer shell. This means they're **reduced**. As they're reduced, they **oxidise** another substance (it's a redox reaction) — so they're **oxidising agents**.

$$X + e^- \rightarrow X^-$$
ox. number:　0　　　　　−1

2) As you go down the group, the atoms become **larger** so the outer electrons are **further** from the nucleus. The outer electrons are also **shielded** more from the attraction of the positive nucleus, because there are more inner electrons. This makes it harder for larger atoms to attract the electron needed to form an ion (despite the increased charge on the nucleus), so larger atoms are less reactive.

3) Another way of saying that the halogens get **less reactive** down the group is to say that they become **less oxidising**.

Halogens **Displace** Less Reactive Halide Ions from Solution

1) The halogens' **relative oxidising strengths** can be seen in their **displacement reactions** with halide ions. For example, if you mix bromine water, $Br_{2\,(aq)}$, with potassium iodide solution, the bromine displaces the iodide ions (it oxidises them), giving iodine (I_2) and potassium bromide solution, $KBr_{(aq)}$.

$$Br_{2(aq)} + 2I^-_{(aq)} \rightarrow 2Br^-_{(aq)} + I_{2(aq)}$$
Oxidation number of Br:　0　　　　　　→　−1
Oxidation number of I:　　　　−1　　→　　　　0

2) When these displacement reactions happen, there are **colour changes** — you can see what happens by following them. Iodine water ($I_{2\,(aq)}$) is **brown** and bromine water ($Br_{2\,(aq)}$) is **orange**.

3) You can make the changes easier to see by shaking the reaction mixture with an **organic solvent** like hexane. The halogen that's present will dissolve readily in the organic solvent, which settles out as a distinct layer above the aqueous solution. A **violet/pink** colour shows the presence of **iodine**. An **orange/red** colour shows **bromine**, and a **very pale yellow/green** shows **chlorine**.

hexane layer
aqueous layer

4) Here are the colour changes you'll see:

	Potassium chloride solution $KCl_{(aq)}$ – colourless	Potassium bromide solution $KBr_{(aq)}$ – colourless	Potassium iodide solution $KI_{(aq)}$ – colourless
Chlorine water $Cl_{2\,(aq)}$ – colourless	no reaction	orange/red solution (Br_2) formed with organic solvent	violet/pink solution (I_2) formed with organic solvent
Bromine water $Br_{2\,(aq)}$ – orange	no reaction	no reaction	violet/pink solution (I_2) formed with organic solvent
Iodine solution $I_{2\,(aq)}$ – brown	no reaction	no reaction	no reaction

Group 7 — The Halogens

Displacement Reactions Can Help to Identify Solutions

These displacement reactions can be used to help **identify** which halogen (or halide) is present in a solution.

A **halogen** will **displace a halide** from solution if the halide is **below it** in the Periodic Table, e.g.

You can also say a halogen will **oxidise** a halide if the halide is below it in the Periodic Table.

Periodic table	Displacement reaction	Ionic equation
Cl	chlorine (Cl_2) will displace bromide (Br^-) and iodide (I^-)	$Cl_{2(aq)} + 2Br^-_{(aq)} \rightarrow 2Cl^-_{(aq)} + Br_{2(aq)}$ $Cl_{2(aq)} + 2I^-_{(aq)} \rightarrow 2Cl^-_{(aq)} + I_{2(aq)}$
Br	bromine (Br_2) will displace iodide (I^-)	$Br_{2(aq)} + 2I^-_{(aq)} \rightarrow 2Br^-_{(aq)} + I_{2(aq)}$
I	no reaction with F^-, Cl^-, Br^-	

Silver Nitrate Solution is used to Test for Halides

The test for halides is dead easy. First you add **dilute nitric acid** to remove ions that might interfere with the test. Then you just add **silver nitrate solution** ($AgNO_{3\,(aq)}$). A **precipitate** is formed (of the silver halide).

$$Ag^+_{(aq)} + X^-_{(aq)} \rightarrow AgX_{(s)} \text{ ...where X is Cl, Br or I}$$

1) The **colour** of the precipitate identifies the halide.
2) Then to be extra sure, you can test your results by adding **ammonia solution**. (Each silver halide has a different solubility in ammonia.)

SILVER NITRATE TEST FOR HALIDE IONS...

Chloride Cl^-: white precipitate, dissolves in dilute $NH_{3(aq)}$

Bromide Br^-: cream precipitate, dissolves in conc. $NH_{3(aq)}$

Iodide I^-: yellow precipitate, insoluble in conc. $NH_{3(aq)}$

Practice Questions

Q1 Describe the trend in boiling points as you go down Group 7.

Q2 What do you see when potassium iodide is added to bromine water?

Q3 Write the ionic equation for the reaction that happens when chlorine is added to a solution of iodide ions.

Q4 How would you test whether an aqueous solution contained chloride ions?

Exam Questions

Q1 a) Write an ionic equation for the reaction between iodine solution and sodium astatide (NaAt). [1 mark]
b) For the equation in (a), deduce which substance is oxidised. [1 mark]

Q2 Describe the test you would carry out in order to distinguish between solid samples of sodium chloride and sodium bromide using silver nitrate solution and aqueous ammonia. State your observations and write equations for the reactions which occur. [6 marks]

Q3 The halogen below iodine in Group 7 is astatine (At). Predict, giving an explanation:
a) the physical state of astatine at r.t.p., [3 marks]
b) whether or not silver astatide will dissolve in concentrated ammonia solution. [3 marks]

Don't skip this page — it could cost you £15 000...

Let me explain... the other night I was watching Who Wants to Be a Millionaire, and this question was on for £32 000:

Which of the these elements is a halogen?
A Argon   B Nitrogen
C Fluorine   D Sodium

Bet Mr Redmond from Wiltshire wishes he paid more attention in Chemistry now, eh. Ha sucker...

Disproportionation and Water Treatment

Here's comes another page jam-packed with golden nuggets of halogen fun. Oh yes, I kid you not. This page is the Alton Towers of AS Chemistry... white-knuckle excitement all the way...

Halogens undergo **Disproportionation** with Alkalis

The halogens will react with cold dilute alkali solutions.
In these reactions, the halogen is simultaneously oxidised and reduced (called **disproportionation**)...

$$X_2 + 2NaOH \rightarrow NaXO + NaX + H_2O$$

Ionic equation:
$$X_2 + 2OH^- \rightarrow XO^- + X^- + H_2O$$

Oxidation number of X: 0 $+1$ -1

The halogens (except fluorine) can exist in a wide range of oxidation states. E.g. chlorine can exist as: ⟶

-1	0	+1
Cl^-	Cl_2	ClO^-
chloride	chlorine	chlorate(I)

Chlorine and *Sodium Hydroxide* make Bleach

If you mix chlorine gas with sodium hydroxide at **room temperature**, the above reaction takes place and you get **sodium chlorate(I) solution**, $NaClO_{(aq)}$, which just happens to be common household **bleach**.

$$2NaOH_{(aq)} + Cl_{2(aq)} \rightarrow NaClO_{(aq)} + NaCl_{(aq)} + H_2O_{(l)}$$

Oxidation number: 0 $+1$ -1

The oxidation number of Cl goes up <u>and</u> down so, you guessed it, it's <u>disproportionation</u>. Hurray.

The sodium chlorate(I) solution (bleach) has loads of uses — it's used in **water treatment**, to bleach **paper** and **textiles**... and it's good for **cleaning toilets**, too. Handy...

Chlorine is used to Kill Bacteria in Water

<u>When you mix chlorine with water</u>, it undergoes disproportionation.
You end up with a mixture of hydrochloric acid and **chloric(I) acid** (also called hypochlorous acid).

$$Cl_{2(g)} + H_2O_{(l)} \rightleftharpoons HCl_{(aq)} + HClO_{(aq)}$$

Oxidation number of Cl: 0 -1 $+1$
                      hydrochloric acid   chloric(I) acid

Aqueous chloric(I) acid **ionises** to make **chlorate(I) ions** (also called hypochlorite ions).

$$HClO_{(aq)} + H_2O_{(l)} \rightleftharpoons ClO^-_{(aq)} + H_3O^+_{(aq)}$$

Chlorate(I) ions **kill bacteria**.

So, **adding chlorine** (or a compound containing chlorate(I) ions) to water can make it safe to **drink** or **swim** in.

Disproportionation and Water Treatment

Chlorine in Water — There are Benefits, Risks and Ethical Implications

1) Clean drinking water is amazingly important — around the world almost **two million people die** every year from waterborne diseases like cholera, typhoid and dysentery because they have to drink dirty water.

2) In the UK now we're lucky, because our drinking water is **treated** to make it safe. **Chlorine** is an important part of water treatment:

Brian gives Susie the water treatment

- It **kills disease-causing microorganisms** (see previous page).
- Some chlorine remains in the water and **prevents reinfection** further down the supply.
- It prevents the growth of **algae**, eliminating **bad tastes** and **smells**, and **removes discolouration** caused by organic compounds.

3) However, there are risks from using chlorine to treat water:

- **Chlorine gas is very harmful** if it's breathed in — it irritates the **respiratory system**. **Liquid chlorine** on the skin or eyes causes severe **chemical burns**. Accidents involving chlorine could be really serious, or fatal.
- Water contains a variety of organic compounds, e.g. from the decomposition of plants. Chlorine reacts with these compounds to form **chlorinated hydrocarbons**, e.g. chloromethane (CH_3Cl) — and many of these chlorinated hydrocarbons are carcinogenic (cancer-causing). However, this increased cancer risk is small compared to the risks from untreated water — a cholera epidemic, say, could kill thousands of people.

4) There are ethical considerations too. We don't get a **choice** about having our water chlorinated — some people object to this as forced 'mass medication'.

And Some Areas Have Fluoridated Water

In some areas of the UK **fluoride ions** are also added to drinking water. Health officials recommend this because it helps to prevent **tooth decay** — there's **loads** of good evidence for this.

There's a **small** amount of evidence linking fluoridated water to a slightly increased risk of some **bone cancers**. Most **toothpaste** is fluoridated, so some people think extra fluoride ions in water is unnecessary.

Practice Questions

Q1 Write the equation for the reaction of chlorine with water. State underneath the oxidation numbers of the chlorine.

Q2 How is common household bleach formed?

Q3 What are the benefits of adding chlorine to drinking water?

Exam Questions

Q1 If chlorine gas and sodium hydroxide are allowed to mix at room temperature, sodium chlorate(I) is formed.

   a) This is a disproportionation reaction. Give the ionic equation for the reaction and use it to explain what is meant by disproportionation. [4 marks]

   b) Give two uses of sodium chlorate(I). [2 marks]

Q2 Iodide ions react with chlorate(I) ions and water to form iodine, chloride ions and hydroxide ions.

   a) Write a balanced equation for this reaction. [2 marks]

   b) Show by use of oxidation states which substance has been oxidised and which has been reduced. [2 marks]

   c) The reaction mixture is shaken with an organic solvent. What colour solution is formed with the organic solvent? [1 mark]

Remain seated until the page comes to a halt. Please exit to the right...

Oooh, what a lovely page, if I do say so myself. I bet the question of how bleach is made and how chlorine reacts with sodium hydroxide has plagued your mind since childhood. Well now you know. And remember... anything that chlorine can do, bromine and iodine can generally do as well. Eeee... it's just fun, fun, fun all the way.

Basic Stuff

This section's all about organic chemistry... carbon compounds, in other words. Read on...

There are **Loads of Ways** of **Representing** Organic Compounds

TYPE OF FORMULA	WHAT IT SHOWS YOU	FORMULA FOR BUTAN-1-OL
<u>General formula</u>	An algebraic formula that can describe **any member** of a family of compounds.	$C_nH_{2n+1}OH$ (for all alcohols)
<u>Empirical formula</u>	The **simplest ratio** of atoms of each element in a compound (cancel the numbers down if possible). (So ethane, C_2H_6, has the empirical formula CH_3.)	$C_4H_{10}O$
<u>Molecular formula</u>	The **actual** number of atoms of each element in a molecule, with any **functional groups** indicated.	C_4H_9OH
<u>Structural formula</u>	Shows the atoms **carbon by carbon**, with the attached hydrogens and functional groups.	$CH_3CH_2CH_2CH_2OH$ or $CH_3(CH_2)_3OH$
<u>Displayed formula</u>	Shows how all the atoms are **arranged**, and all the bonds between them.	$H-\overset{\overset{H}{\mid}}{\underset{\underset{H}{\mid}}{C}}-\overset{\overset{H}{\mid}}{\underset{\underset{H}{\mid}}{C}}-\overset{\overset{H}{\mid}}{\underset{\underset{H}{\mid}}{C}}-\overset{\overset{H}{\mid}}{\underset{\underset{H}{\mid}}{C}}-OH$
<u>Skeletal formula</u>	Shows the **bonds** of the carbon skeleton **only**, with any functional groups. The hydrogen and carbon atoms aren't shown. This is handy for drawing large complicated structures, like cyclic hydrocarbons.	⟍⟋⟍⟋OH

> A functional group is a reactive part of a molecule — it gives it many of its chemical properties.

The **Alkanes** are the Simplest **Group** of Organic Compounds

1) Organic chemistry is more about **groups** of similar chemicals than individual compounds.

2) These groups are called **homologous series**. A homologous series is a bunch of compounds that have the same **functional group** and **general formula**. Consecutive members of a homologous series differ by $-CH_2-$.

3) The simplest homologous series is the **alkanes**. They're **straight chain** molecules that contain only **carbon** and **hydrogen** atoms. There's a lot more about the alkanes on page 54.

4) The **general formula** for alkanes is C_nH_{2n+2}. So the first alkane in the series is $C_1H_{(2 \times 1)+2} = CH_4$ (you don't need to write the 1 in C_1), the second is $C_2H_{(2 \times 2)+2} = C_2H_6$, the seventeenth is $C_{17}H_{(2 \times 17)+2} = C_{17}H_{38}$, and so on...

5) You need to know the names of the **first ten** alkanes.

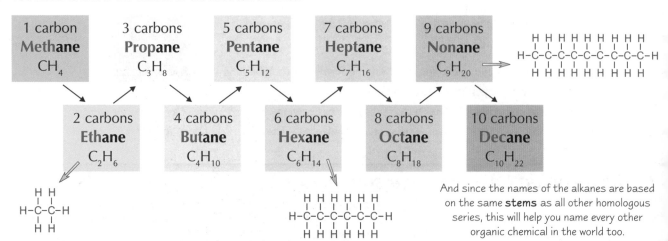

1 carbon **Methane** CH_4	3 carbons **Propane** C_3H_8	5 carbons **Pentane** C_5H_{12}	7 carbons **Heptane** C_7H_{16}	9 carbons **Nonane** C_9H_{20}
2 carbons **Ethane** C_2H_6	4 carbons **Butane** C_4H_{10}	6 carbons **Hexane** C_6H_{14}	8 carbons **Octane** C_8H_{18}	10 carbons **Decane** $C_{10}H_{22}$

And since the names of the alkanes are based on the same **stems** as all other homologous series, this will help you name every other organic chemical in the world too.

Basic Stuff

Nomenclature is a Fancy Word for the Naming of Organic Compounds

You can name any organic compound using these **rules** of nomenclature.

1) Count the carbon atoms in the **longest continuous chain** — this gives you the stem.

2) The **main functional group** of the molecule usually gives you the end of the name (the **suffix**) — see the table below.

No. of C	1	2	3	4	5	6
Stem	meth-	eth-	prop-	but-	pent-	hex-

Homologous series	Prefix or Suffix	Example
alkanes	-ane	propane $CH_3CH_2CH_3$
branched alkanes	alkyl- (-yl)	methylpropane $CH_3CH(CH_3)CH_3$
alkenes	-ene	propene $CH_3CH=CH_2$
halogenoalkanes	chloro- bromo- iodo-	chlorethane CH_3CH_2Cl
alcohols	-ol	ethanol CH_3CH_2OH
aldehydes	-al	ethanal CH_3CHO
ketones	-one	propanone CH_3COCH_3
cycloalkanes	cyclo- -ane	cyclohexane C_6H_{12}
arenes	benzene	ethylbenzene $C_6H_5C_2H_5$
esters	alkyl -oate	propyl ethanoate $CH_3COOCH_2CH_2CH_3$
carboxylic acids	-oic acid	ethanoic acid CH_3COOH

3) Number the **longest** carbon chain so that the main functional group has the lowest possible number. If there's more than one longest chain, pick the one with the **most side-chains**.

4) Any side-chains or less important functional groups are added as prefixes at the start of the name. Put them in **alphabetical** order, with the **number** of the carbon atom each is attached to.

5) If there's more than one **identical** side-chain or functional group, use **di-** (2), **tri-** (3) or **tetra-** (4) before that part of the name — but ignore this when working out the alphabetical order.

Example:

$CH_3CH(CH_3)CH(CH_2CH_3)C(CH_3)_2OH$

1) Longest chain is **5 carbons**   pent-

2) Main functional group is **-OH**   pentanol

3) **Number** the longest carbon chain so that -OH has **lowest** possible number (and you have most side-chains).   **pentan-2-ol**

4) Add **prefixes** for side-chains.   **3-ethyl-2,4-dimethylpentan-2-ol**

Longest chain with most side-chains

Practice Questions

Q1 Explain the difference between molecular formulas and structural formulas.

Q2 Draw the displayed formula for octane. Now write the structural formula.

Q3 In what order should prefixes be listed in the name of an organic compound?

Q4 Draw the displayed formula of 2,4,6-triethylhexan-3-ol.

Q5 What is meant by the term 'homologous series'?

Q6 Write down the structural formula of the 8th compound in the homologous series with general formula $C_nH_{2n+1}OH$.

Exam Questions

Q1 1-bromobutane is prepared from butan-1-ol in this reaction: $C_4H_9OH + NaBr + H_2SO_4 \rightarrow C_4H_9Br + NaHSO_4 + H_2O$

   a) Draw the displayed formulae for butan-1-ol and 1-bromobutane.   [2 marks]

   b) What is the functional group in butan-1-ol and why is it necessary to state its position on the carbon chain?   [2 marks]

Q2 Give the systematic names of the following compounds.

   A   B   C   [6 marks]

It's as easy as 1,2,3-trimethylpentan-2-ol...

The best thing to do now is find some random organic compounds and work out their names using the rules. Then have a bash at it the other way around — read the name and draw the compound. It might seem a bit tedious now, but come the exam, you'll be thanking me. Talking of exams — read the questions carefully and check what type of formula they want.

Isomerism

Isomers have the same molecular formula, but different arrangements of atoms.
There are two main types of isomerism — structural isomerism and stereoisomerism.

Structural Isomers have different Structural Arrangements of Atoms

In structural isomers, the **molecular formula** is the same, but the **structural formula** is different.
There are **three** different types of structural isomer:

1. CHAIN ISOMERS

The **carbon skeleton** can be arranged differently — for example, as a **straight chain**, or **branched** in different ways.

These isomers have **similar chemical properties** — but their **physical properties**, like boiling point, will be **different** because of the change in shape of the molecule.

C_4H_{10}

butane

methylpropane

$CH_3CH_2CH_2CH_3$

$CH_3CHCH_3CH_3$

2. POSITIONAL ISOMERS

The **skeleton** and the **functional group** could be the same, only with the group attached to a **different carbon atom**.

These also have **different physical properties**, and the **chemical properties** might be **different** too.

$C_4H_{10}O$

butan-1-ol

butan-2-ol

$CH_3CH_2CH_2CH_2OH$

$CH_3CH_2CHOHCH_3$ OH

3. FUNCTIONAL GROUP ISOMERS

The same atoms can be arranged into **different functional groups**.

These have very **different physical** and **chemical** properties.

$C_4H_{10}O$

butan-1-ol

ethoxyethane

$CH_3(CH_2)_3OH$

$CH_3CH_2OCH_2CH_3$

Don't be Fooled — What Looks Like an Isomer Might Not Be

Atoms can rotate as much as they like around single **C–C bonds**.

Remember this when you work out structural isomers — sometimes what looks like an isomer, isn't.

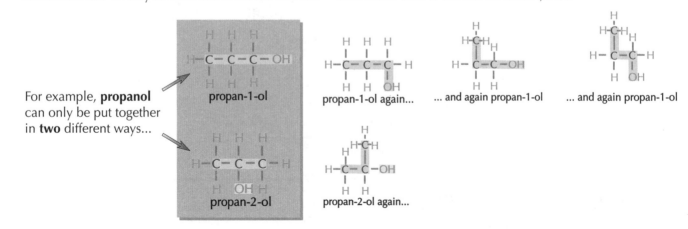

For example, **propanol** can only be put together in **two** different ways...

propan-1-ol

propan-1-ol again...   ... and again propan-1-ol   ... and again propan-1-ol

propan-2-ol

propan-2-ol again...

Isomerism

E/Z isomerism is a Type of Stereoisomerism

1) **Stereoisomers** have the same structural formula but a **different arrangement** in space.
   (Just bear with me for a moment... that will become clearer, I promise.)

2) Some **alkenes** have stereoisomers — this is because there's a **lack of rotation** around the C=C double bond (see p62). When the double-bonded carbon atoms each have **two different atoms** or **groups** attached to them, you get an '**E-isomer**' and a '**Z-isomer**'.
   For example, the double-bonded carbon atoms in but-2-ene each have an **H** and a **CH₃** group attached.

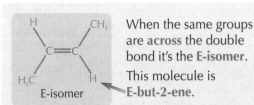

When the same groups are **across** the double bond it's the **E-isomer**.
This molecule is **E-but-2-ene**.

When the same groups are **both above** or **both below** the double bond it's the Z-isomer.
This molecule is **Z-but-2-ene**.

3) E/Z isomerism is sometimes called **cis-trans isomerism**, where '**cis**' means the **Z-isomer**, and '**trans**' means the **E-isomer**. So E-but-2-ene can be called trans-but-2-ene, and Z-but-2-ene can be called cis-but-2-ene.

4) **BUT**, you can't use the cis-trans system if there are **more than two** different groups (other than hydrogen atoms) attached around the double bond.

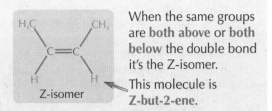

This could be **trans-1-bromo-1-fluoropropene**, because the **Br** and **CH₃** are on **opposite** sides, or it could be **cis-1-bromo-1-fluoropropene**, because the **F** and **CH₃** are on the same side...

5) The E/Z system keeps on working though. Each of the groups linked to the double-bonded carbons is given a **priority**. If the two carbon atoms have their 'higher priority group' on **opposite** sides, then it's an **E isomer**. If the two carbon atoms have their 'higher priority group' on the **same** side, then it's a **Z isomer**. (You don't need to know the rules for deciding the order of these priorities.)

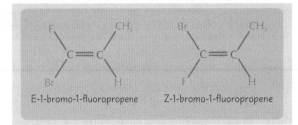

E-1-bromo-1-fluoropropene   Z-1-bromo-1-fluoropropene

6) In the E/Z system, Br has a **higher priority** than F, so the names depend on where the Br atom is in relation to the CH₃ group (which has a higher priority than the H atom).

Practice Questions

Q1 What are isomers?

Q2 Name the three types of structural isomerism.

Q3 What is a positional isomer?

Q4 What is stereoisomerism?

Q5 Why doesn't but-1-ene show E/Z isomerism?

Exam Question

Q1 a) There are five chain isomers of the alkane C_6H_{14}.
    (i) Draw and name all five isomers of C_6H_{14}. [10 marks]
    (ii) Explain what is meant by the term 'chain isomerism'. [2 marks]

  b) There are four isomers of the alkene C_3H_5Cl.
    (i) Draw and name the pair of stereoisomers. [4 marks]
    (ii) Draw and name the two isomers which do not show stereoisomerism. [4 marks]

  c) Alkanes and alkenes are both examples of a homologous series. What is a homologous series? [2 marks]

Human structural isomers...

Atom Economy and Percentage Yield

How to make a subject like chemistry even more exciting — introduce the word 'economy'...

The **Theoretical Yield** of a Product is the **Maximum** you could get

1) The **theoretical yield** is the **mass of product** that **should** be made in a reaction if **no** chemicals are '**lost**' in the process. You can use the **masses of reactants** and a **balanced equation** to calculate the theoretical yield for a reaction.

2) The **actual** mass of product (the **actual yield**) is always **less** than the theoretical yield. Some chemicals are always 'lost', e.g. some solution gets left on filter paper, or is lost during transfers between containers.

3) The **percentage yield** is the **actual** amount of product you collect, written as a percentage of the theoretical yield. You can work out the percentage yield with this formula:

$$\text{Percentage yield} = \frac{\text{actual yield}}{\text{theoretical yield}} \times 100\%$$

> **Example:** Ethanol can be oxidised to form ethanal: $C_2H_5OH + [O] \rightarrow CH_3CHO + H_2O$
> 9.2 g of ethanol was reacted with an oxidising agent in excess and 2.1 g of ethanal was produced. Calculate the theoretical yield and the percentage yield.
>
> Number of moles = mass of substance ÷ molar mass
> Moles of C_2H_5OH = 9.2 ÷ [(2 × 12) + (5 × 1) + 16 + 1] = 9.2 ÷ 46 = 0.2 moles
> 1 mole of C_2H_5OH produces 1 mole of CH_3CHO, so 0.2 moles of C_2H_5OH will produce 0.2 moles of CH_3CHO.
> M of CH_3CHO = (2 × 12) + (4 × 1) + 16 = 44 g mol^{-1}
>
> Theoretical yield (mass of CH_3CHO) = number of moles × M = 0.2 × 44 = **8.8 g**
>
> So, if the actual yield was 2.1 g, the percentage yield = $\frac{\text{actual yield}}{\text{theoretical yield}} \times 100\% = \frac{2.1}{8.8} \times 100\% \approx \mathbf{24\%}$

Atom Economy is a Measure of the **Efficiency** of a Reaction

1) The **percentage yield** tells you how wasteful the **process** is — it's based on how much of the product is lost because of things like reactions not completing or losses during collection and purification.

2) But percentage yield doesn't measure how wasteful the **reaction** itself is. A reaction that has a 100% yield could still be very wasteful if a lot of the atoms from the **reactants** wind up in **by-products** rather than the **desired product**.

3) **Atom economy** is a measure of the proportion of reactant **atoms** that become part of the desired product (rather than by-products) in the **balanced** chemical equation. It's calculated using this formula:

$$\% \text{ atom economy} = \frac{\text{molecular mass of desired product}}{\text{sum of molecular masses of all products}} \times 100\%$$

4) In an **addition reaction**, the reactants **combine** to form a **single product**. The atom economy for addition reactions is **always 100%** since no atoms are wasted.

For example, ethene (C_2H_4) and hydrogen react to form ethane (C_2H_6) in an addition reaction:

$$C_2H_4 + H_2 \rightarrow C_2H_6$$

The **only product** is ethane — the desired product. So no reactant atoms are wasted — the atom economy is **100%**.

5) A **substitution reaction** is one where some atoms from one reactant are **swapped** with atoms from another reactant. This type of reaction **always** results in **at least two products** — the desired product and at least one by-product.

An example is the reaction of bromomethane (CH_3Br) with sodium hydroxide (NaOH) to make methanol (CH_3OH):

$$CH_3Br + NaOH \rightarrow CH_3OH + NaBr$$

This is **more wasteful** than an addition reaction because the Na and Br atoms are not part of the desired product.

$$\% \text{ atom economy} = \frac{\text{molecular mass of desired product}}{\text{sum of molecular masses of all products}} \times 100\%$$

$$= \frac{M_r(CH_3OH)}{M_r(CH_3OH) + M_r(NaBr)} \times 100\%$$

$$= \frac{(12 + (3 \times 1) + 16 + 1)}{(12 + (3 \times 1) + 16 + 1) + (23 + 80)} \times 100\% = \frac{32}{32 + 103} \times 100\% = \mathbf{23.7\%}$$

Always make sure you're using a balanced equation.

Atom Economy and Percentage Yield

Reactions can Have **High Percentage Yields** and **Low Atom Economies**

Example: 0.475 g of CH_3Br reacts with an excess of NaOH in this reaction: $CH_3Br + NaOH \rightarrow CH_3OH + NaBr$
0.153 g of CH_3OH is produced. What is the percentage yield?

Number of moles = mass of substance ÷ molar mass

Moles of CH_3Br = 0.475 ÷ (12 + 3 × 1 + 80) = 0.475 ÷ 95 = **0.005 moles**

The reactant : product ratio is 1 : 1, so the maximum number of moles of CH_3OH is **0.005**.

Theoretical yield = 0.005 × $M_r(CH_3OH)$ = 0.005 × (12 + (3 × 1) + 16 + 1) = 0.005 × 32 = **0.160 g**

$$\text{percentage yield} = \frac{\text{actual yield}}{\text{theoretical yield}} \times 100\% = \frac{0.153}{0.160} \times 100\% = \textbf{95.6\%}$$

So this reaction has a **very high percentage yield**, but, as you saw on the previous page, the **atom economy** is **low**.

It's Important to Develop Reactions with **High Atom Economies**

1) Companies in the chemical industry will often choose to use reactions with high atom economies. High atom economy has **environmental** and **economic benefits**.

2) A **low atom economy** means there's lots of **waste** produced. It costs money to **separate** the desired product from the waste products and more money to dispose of the waste products **safely** so they don't harm the environment.

3) Companies will usually have paid good money to buy the **reactant chemicals**. It's a **waste of money** if a high proportion of them end up as useless products.

Finding uses for the by-products helps to solve some of the problems of low atom economy.

4) Reactions with low atom economies are **less sustainable** (see p90). Many raw materials are in **limited supply**, so it makes sense to use them efficiently so they last as long as possible. Also, waste has to go somewhere — it's better for the environment if less is produced.

Practice Questions

Q1 How many products are there in an addition reaction?

Q2 Does the percentage yield for a reaction always have the same value as the percentage atom economy?

Q3 Why do reactions with high atom economy save chemical companies money and cause less environmental impact?

Exam Questions

Q1 Reactions 1 and 2 below show two possible ways of preparing the compound chloroethane (C_2H_5Cl):

1 $C_2H_5OH + PCl_5 \rightarrow C_2H_5Cl + POCl_3 + HCl$
2 $C_2H_4 + HCl \rightarrow C_2H_5Cl$

a) Which of these is an addition reaction? [1 mark]

b) Calculate the atom economy for reaction 1. [3 marks]

c) Reaction 2 has an atom economy of 100%. Explain why this is, in terms of the products of the reaction. [1 mark]

Q2 Phosphorus trichloride (PCl_3) reacts with chlorine to give phosphorus pentachloride (PCl_5):

$PCl_3 + Cl_2 \rightleftharpoons PCl_5$

a) If 0.275 g of PCl_3 reacts with 0.142 g of chlorine, what is the theoretical yield of PCl_5? [2 marks]

b) When this reaction is performed 0.198 g of PCl_5 is collected. Calculate the percentage yield. [1 mark]

c) Changing conditions such as temperature and pressure will alter the percentage yield of this reaction. Will changing these conditions affect the atom economy? Explain your answer. [2 marks]

I knew a Tommy Conomy once... strange bloke...

These pages shouldn't be too much trouble — you've survived worse already. Make sure that you get plenty of practice using the percentage yield and atom economy formulas. And whatever you do, don't get mixed up between percentage yield (which is to do with the process) and atom economy (which is to do with the reaction).

Alkanes

Alkanes are your basic hydrocarbons — like it says on the tin, they've got hydrogen and they've got carbon.

Alkanes are **Saturated Hydrocarbons**

1) Alkanes have the **general formula C_nH_{2n+2}**.
They've only got **carbon** and **hydrogen** atoms, so they're **hydrocarbons**.

2) Every carbon atom in an alkane has **four single bonds** with other atoms.
It's **impossible** for carbon to make more than four bonds, so alkanes are **saturated**.

Here are a few examples of alkanes —

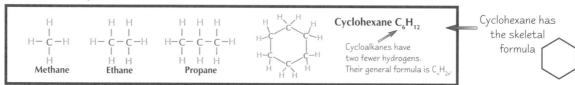

Methane   **Ethane**   **Propane**

Cyclohexane C_6H_{12}

Cycloalkanes have two fewer hydrogens. Their general formula is C_nH_{2n}.

Cyclohexane has the skeletal formula

Alkane Molecules are **Tetrahedral** Around **Each Carbon**

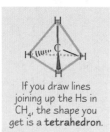

If you draw lines joining up the Hs in CH_4, the shape you get is a **tetrahedron**.

In an alkane molecule, each carbon atom has **four pairs** of **bonding electrons** around it.
They all repel each other **equally**. So the molecule forms a tetrahedral shape around **each carbon**.

Methane
1 tetrahedral carbon

Ethane
2 tetrahedral carbons

Propane
3 tetrahedral carbons

For more about the shapes of molecules, see page 32.

The **Boiling Point** of an Alkane Depends on its **Size** and **Shape**

The smallest alkanes, like methane, are **gases** at room temperature and pressure — they've got very low boiling points.
Larger alkanes are **liquids** — they have higher boiling points.

1) Alkanes have **covalent bonds** inside the molecules. **Between** the molecules, there are **van der Waals** forces which hold them all together.

2) The **longer** the carbon chain, the **stronger** the van der Waals forces. This is because there's **more molecular surface area** and more electrons to interact.

3) So as the molecules get longer, it takes **more energy** to overcome the van der Waals forces and separate them, and the boiling point **rises**.

4) A **branched-chain** alkane has a **lower** boiling point than its straight-chain isomer. Branched-chain alkanes can't **pack closely** together and they have smaller **molecular surface areas** — so the van der Waals forces are reduced.

Example: Isomers of C_4H_{10}

Butane, boiling point = 273 K

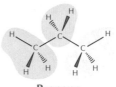

Molecules can pack closely.

Methylpropane, boiling point = 261 K

Close packing isn't possible.

Alkanes Burn **Completely** in Oxygen

1) If you burn (**oxidise**) alkanes with enough **oxygen**, you get **carbon dioxide** and water — this is a **combustion reaction**.

Here's the equation for the combustion of propane — $C_3H_{8(g)} + 5O_{2(g)} \rightarrow 3CO_{2(g)} + 4H_2O_{(g)}$

2) Combustion reactions happen between **gases**, so liquid alkanes have to be **vaporised** first.
Smaller alkanes turn into **gases** more easily (they're more **volatile**), so they'll **burn** more easily too.

3) Larger alkanes release heaps more **energy** per mole because they have more bonds to react.

4) Because they release so much energy when they burn, alkanes make excellent fuels.
Propane is used as a **central heating** and **cooking** fuel. **Butane** is bottled and sold as **camping gas**.
Petrol and **diesel** are both made up of a mixture of alkanes too (and additives).

Alkanes

Burning **Alkanes** In **Limited Oxygen** Produces **Carbon Monoxide**

1) If there isn't much oxygen around, the alkane will still burn, but it will produce **carbon monoxide** and water.

> For example, burning methane with not much O_2 —
> $$2CH_{4(g)} + 3O_{2(g)} \rightarrow 2CO_{(g)} + 4H_2O_{(g)}$$

2) This is a problem because **carbon monoxide** is **poisonous**.

> 1) The **oxygen** in your bloodstream is carried around by **haemoglobin**.
> 2) **Carbon monoxide** is **better** at binding to haemoglobin than oxygen is. So if you breathe in air with a **high concentration** of carbon monoxide it will bind to the haemoglobin in your bloodstream **before** the oxygen can.
> 3) This means that **less oxygen** will reach your cells. You will start to suffer from symptoms associated with **oxygen deprivation** — things like fatigue, headaches, and nausea. At very high concentrations of carbon monoxide it can even be fatal.

3) **Any** appliance that burns alkanes can produce carbon monoxide. This includes things like gas- or oil-fired boilers and heaters, gas stoves, and coal or wood fires. Cars also produce carbon monoxide.

4) All appliances that use an alkane-based fuel need to be **properly ventilated**. They should be checked and maintained regularly, and their sources of ventilation should **never** be blocked.

5) If you have any alkane burning appliances it's a good idea to have a **carbon monoxide detector** around.

Practice Questions

Q1 What's the general formula for alkanes?

Q2 What kind of intermolecular forces are there between alkane molecules?

Q3 Why do straight-chain alkanes have higher boiling points than branched-chain alkanes?

Q4 What are the combustion products of alkanes when there's plenty of oxygen around? And when oxygen is limited?

Exam Questions

Q1 The alkane ethane is a saturated hydrocarbon. It is mostly unreactive, but will react with oxygen in a combustion reaction.

a) What is a saturated hydrocarbon? [2 marks]

b) Write a balanced equation for the complete combustion of ethane. [2 marks]

Q2 Nonane is a hydrocarbon with the formula C_9H_{20}.

a) What homologous series does nonane belong to? [1 mark]

b) Which would you expect to have a higher boiling point, nonane or 2,2,3,3-tetramethylpentane? Explain your answer. [2 marks]

c) When nonane burns in a limited air supply the products are carbon monoxide and water.

(i) Write a balanced equation for the reaction. [1 mark]

(ii) Explain why carbon monoxide is such a dangerous gas. [2 marks]

d) Explain why burning 1 mole of nonane produces more energy than burning 1 mole of methane. [2 marks]

Tetrahedra — aren't they those monsters from Greek mythology...

Alkanes... they don't do much, so there's only so much the examiners can ask you. Which means:
(i) you need to understand exactly why two molecules containing the same atoms can have different boiling points,
(ii) you need to know why burning alkane-based fuels without enough oxygen is dangerous. No excuses now.

Petroleum

Petroleum is just a posh word for crude oil — the black, yukky stuff they get out of the ground from huge oil wells.

Crude Oil *is a Mixture of* Hydrocarbons

1) Petroleum or crude oil is mostly **alkanes**. They range from **smallish alkanes**, like propane, to **massive alkanes** with more than 50 carbons.

2) Crude oil isn't very useful as it is, but you can **separate** it into more useful bits (or **fractions**) by **fractional distillation**.

Here's how fractional distillation works — don't try this at home.

1) First, the crude oil is **vaporised** at about 350 °C.

2) The vaporised crude oil goes into the **fractionating column** and rises up through the trays. The largest hydrocarbons don't **vaporise** at all, because their boiling points are too high — they just run to the bottom and form a gooey **residue**.

3) As the crude oil vapour goes up the fractionating column, it gets **cooler**. Because of the different chain lengths, each fraction **condenses** at a different temperature. The fractions are **drawn off** at different levels in the column.

4) The hydrocarbons with the **lowest boiling points** don't condense. They're drawn off as **gases** at the top of the column.

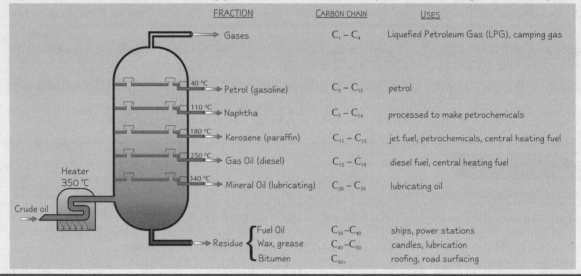

FRACTION	CARBON CHAIN	USES
Gases	$C_1 - C_4$	Liquefied Petroleum Gas (LPG), camping gas
Petrol (gasoline)	$C_5 - C_{12}$	petrol
Naphtha	$C_7 - C_{14}$	processed to make petrochemicals
Kerosene (paraffin)	$C_{11} - C_{15}$	jet fuel, petrochemicals, central heating fuel
Gas Oil (diesel)	$C_{15} - C_{19}$	diesel fuel, central heating fuel
Mineral Oil (lubricating)	$C_{20} - C_{30}$	lubricating oil
Fuel Oil	$C_{30} - C_{40}$	ships, power stations
Wax, grease	$C_{40} - C_{50}$	candles, lubrication
Bitumen	C_{50+}	roofing, road surfacing

3) Most of the fractions are either used as **fuels** or processed to make **petrochemicals**. A **petrochemical** is any compound that is made from crude oil or any of its fractions and is not a fuel.

Heavy Fractions *can be* 'Cracked' *to Make* Smaller Molecules

1) People want loads of the **light** fractions, like petrol and naphtha. They don't want so much of the **heavier** stuff like bitumen though.

2) To meet this demand, the less popular heavier fractions are **cracked**. Cracking is **breaking** long-chain alkanes into **smaller** hydrocarbons. It involves breaking the **C–C bonds**. You could crack **decane** like this —

$$C_{10}H_{22} \rightarrow C_2H_4 + C_8H_{18}$$
decane   ethene   octane

3) The main way of doing this is **catalytic cracking**.

- The heavier fractions are passed over a **catalyst** at a high temperature and a moderate pressure.
- This breaks them up into **smaller molecules**.
- Using a catalyst **cuts costs**, because the reaction can be done at a **lower** temperature and pressure. The catalyst also **speeds** up the reaction, and time is money and all that.

Aromatic hydrocarbons contain benzene rings.

4) This method of cracking gives a high percentage of **branched hydrocarbons** and **aromatic hydrocarbons** — these are particularly useful for making **petrol**.

Petroleum

Hydrocarbons with a High Octane Rating Burn More Smoothly

1) Here's a super-quick whizz through how a **petrol engine** works:
The **fuel/air** mixture is squashed by a **piston** and **ignited** with a spark, creating an **explosion**. This drives the piston up again, turning the **crankshaft**. Four pistons work **one after the other**, so that the engine runs smoothly.

2) The problem is, **straight-chain alkanes** in petrol tend to **auto-ignite** — when the fuel/air mixture is compressed they explode without being ignited by the spark. This extra explosion causes 'knocking' in the engine.

3) To get rid of knocking and make combustion more efficient, **shorter branched-chain alkanes**, **cycloalkanes** and **arenes** are included in petrols, creating a **high octane rating**.

The octane rating of a petrol tells you how likely it is to auto-ignite. The higher the number, the less likely it is to auto-ignite. It's based on a scale where 100% heptane has a rating of 0, and 100% 2,2,4-trimethylpentane has a rating of 100.

Heptane C_7H_{16} (a straight-chain alkane)

2,2,4-trimethylpentane $C(CH_3)_3CH_2CH(CH_3)_2$ (a branched-chain alkane)

Straight-Chain Alkanes are Made Into Branched or Cyclic Hydrocarbons

Fuel manufacturers convert some of the **straight-chain alkanes** into **branched-chain alkanes** and **cyclic hydrocarbons** using isomerisation and reforming.

ISOMERISATION — STRAIGHT-CHAIN TO BRANCHED-CHAIN

Isomerisation occurs when you heat **straight-chain** alkanes with a **catalyst** stuck on inert aluminium oxide. The alkanes break up and join back together as **branched isomers**.

A **molecular sieve** (zeolite) is used to separate the isomers. **Straight-chain** molecules go through the sieve and are **recycled**.

$CH_3CH_2CH_2CH_3 \xrightarrow{Pt} H_3C-CH(CH_3)-CH_3$

butane → 2-methylpropane

REFORMING — STRAIGHT-CHAIN TO CYCLIC

Reforming converts **alkanes** into **cyclic hydrocarbons**.

It uses a **catalyst** made of **platinum** and another metal. Again, you need to stick the catalyst on inert aluminium oxide.

$CH_3CH_2CH_2CH_2CH_2CH_3 \xrightarrow[metal]{Pt\ and}$ cyclohexane $+ H_2 \rightarrow$ benzene $+ 3H_2$

hexane

Practice Questions

Q1 What is the naphtha fraction of crude oil used for?

Q2 What is cracking?

Q3 Explain why isomerisation is carried out.

Exam Question

Q1 Crude oil is a source of fuels and petrochemicals. It's vaporised and separated into fractions using fractional distillation.
a) Some heavier fractions are processed using cracking.
(i) Give one reason why cracking is carried out. [2 marks]
(ii) Write an equation for the cracking of dodecane, $C_{12}H_{26}$. [1 mark]

b) Some hydrocarbons are processed using isomerisation or reforming, producing a petrol with a high octane rating. Petrols with a high octane rating burn more efficiently.
(i) What kinds of compounds are desirable for a petrol that will burn efficiently? [3 marks]
(ii) What effect do they have on the petrol's performance? [1 mark]
(iii) Draw and name two isomers formed from pentane by isomerisation. [4 marks]

Crude oil — not the kind of oil you could take home to meet your mother...

This ain't the most exciting page in the history of the known universe. Although in a galaxy far, far away there may be lots of pages on even more boring topics. But, that's neither here nor there, cos you've got to learn the stuff anyway. Get fractional distillation and cracking straight in your brain and make sure you know why people bother to do them.

Fossil Fuels

Ah, fossils... so this is going to be a cool page about dinosaurs and stuff, I expect...

Fossil Fuels are Incredibly Useful — We Rely on Them for Loads of Things...

The three fossil fuels — coal, oil and natural gas — are major fuels. We use them to provide...

ENERGY

1) The combustion of fossil fuels is very **exothermic** — they give out large amounts of energy when they burn, which is why they make great **fuels**.
2) Different **alkanes** are used as fuels for various forms of transport (see p56).
3) Fossil fuels are burned to generate **electricity** in most of the world's **power stations**.

RAW MATERIALS

1) Coal, oil and gas aren't just used as fuels, though. They're also important **raw materials** in the chemical industry. Hydrocarbons obtained from fossil fuels — especially oil — are used, either on their own or with other chemicals, for a whole range of purposes.
2) For example, almost all modern plastics are polymers (see p63) made with organic chemicals from fossil fuels.
3) Other products of the petrochemical industry include **solvents**, **detergents**, **adhesives** and **lubricants**.

In Fact... Maybe We Rely on Them Too Much

Fossil fuels are really useful — but there are a couple of major problems with them...

Burning Fuels Makes Greenhouse Gases

1) Right now we're burning more **carbon-based fossil fuels** (e.g. in transport, power stations etc.) than ever before. This is one factor that's helping to cause an increase in the amount of **carbon dioxide** in the atmosphere.
2) Carbon dioxide is a **greenhouse gas**. The extra carbon dioxide we're producing is contributing to **global warming** and **climate change** by enhancing the **greenhouse effect**. See pages 92-93.

Fossil Fuels are Non-Renewable

1) There's a finite amount of fossil fuels — and they're **running out**. Oil will be the first to go — and as it gets really scarce, it'll become more expensive. It's not **sustainable** to keep using fossil fuels willy-nilly (see page 90 for more on sustainability).
2) The developed world relies heavily on fossil fuels to produce **energy** for transport, heating and electricity generation, and to make **chemicals** like plastics and fibres.
3) Some estimates suggest that if we keep using them up at the rate we are doing, there could be just **45 years** worth of oil, **70 years** worth of gas and **250 years** worth of coal left in the ground. And we could run out even sooner, because countries like **China** and **India** are developing rapidly and increasing their energy needs. New supplies may be found, but eventually they'll run out too.
4) There are **alternative sources** of energy that can be used (see the next page), and most of the chemicals currently made from crude oil can be made from **coal** or **plants**. But while there are still reserves of fossil fuels most businesses aren't keen to spend money developing these alternatives.

A couple of overturned bins make a great alternative to motor transport

Fossil Fuels

There are Potential **Alternatives** to Fossil Fuels

So we need to do something about the fuel situation — and there are various options. **Plants** could be an important source of fuels for the future. They're great, because they're **renewable** — you can grow more if you need to.

BIOETHANOL

1) Ethanol can be used to fuel cars, either on its own or added to petrol. **Bioethanol** is ethanol that's produced from plants — it's made by the **fermentation of sugar** from crops such as maize.

2) Bioethanol's thought of as being **carbon neutral** — in other words, it has **no overall carbon emission** into the atmosphere. That's because all the CO_2 **released** when the fuel is burned was **removed** by the crop as it grew.

3) **BUT** — there are still carbon emissions if you consider the **whole** process. Making the fertilisers and powering agricultural machinery will probably involve burning fossil fuels. It's still better than petrol though, and it does conserve crude oil supplies.

BIODIESEL

1) **Biodiesel** is another fuel that can come from plants. As the name suggests, it can be used in **diesel engines** — you can use 100% biodiesel or a mixture of biodiesel and conventional diesel.

2) It's made by refining renewable **fats and oils**, such as vegetable oils (biodiesel can even be made from used restaurant fryer oil).

3) Like bioethanol, biodiesel can be a **carbon neutral** fuel (but the same big **BUT** from point 3 above applies here, too).

There are some potential problems with using crops to make fuels:

- It's possible that **developed countries** (like us) will create a huge demand as they try and find fossil fuel alternatives. Poorer **developing countries** (in South America, say) will use this as a way of **earning money** and rush to convert their farming land to produce these 'crops for fuels', which may mean they won't grow enough **food** to eat.

- There are also worries that in some places **forests** are being **cleared** to make room for biofuel crops. The crops absorb **far less CO_2** than the forest did — so this defeats one of the main objects of growing biofuels.

Practice Questions

Q1 Describe two uses of fossil fuels.

Q2 Describe two disadvantages of using fossil fuels.

Q3 What is the raw material for the production of bioethanol?

Exam Questions

Q1 Various alternative fuels for transport have been proposed. One of these is 'bioethanol' made from sugar.

    a) Name the process used to produce ethanol from sugar.   [1 mark]

    b) Explain why ethanol produced this way is considered to be carbon neutral.   [2 marks]

    c) Describe the possible negative effect on developing countries of growing crops for conversion to fuel.   [2 marks]

Q2 Coal, oil and natural gas are described as fossil fuels.

    a) Why do coal, oil and gas make good fuels?   [1 mark]

    b) Why does fossil fuel use contribute to global warming?   [2 marks]

    c) Why are fossil fuels described as non-renewable?   [2 marks]

    d) Describe one other use of fossil fuels, other than being burned as fuels.   [1 mark]

[Insert predictable 'fossil' joke about the age of your teacher here]

The question of what we're going to do to replace fossil fuels is a pretty vital one — because they are going to run out and, in the case of oil at least, that could well happen within your lifetime. Biofuels look like they could be an answer but they're hardly problem-free either. And as if the world's fuel problems weren't enough, you've got AS exams coming up too...

Alkanes — Substitution Reactions

Oooh, eh... mechanisms. You might like them. You might not. But you've gotta learn 'em.
Reactions don't happen instantaneously — there are often a few steps. And mechanisms show you what they are.

There are **Two Types** of Bond Fission — **Homolytic** and **Heterolytic**

Breaking a covalent bond is called **bond fission**. A single covalent bond is a shared pair of electrons between two atoms. It can break in two ways:

Heterolytic Fission:
In heterolytic fission **two different** substances are formed — a positively charged **cation** (X^+), and a negatively charged **anion** (Y^-).

$$X \div Y \rightarrow X^+ + Y^-$$

('hetero' means 'different')

Homolytic Fission:
In homolytic fission two electrically uncharged 'radicals' are formed. Radicals are particles that have an unpaired electron.

$$X \cdot \cdot Y \rightarrow X\cdot + Y\cdot$$

Because of the unpaired electron, these radicals are very reactive.

A double-headed curly arrow shows that a pair of electrons move. A single-headed curly arrow shows the movement of a single electron. Makes sense.

Halogens React with **Alkanes**, Forming **Halogenoalkanes**

1) Halogens react with alkanes in **photochemical** reactions. Photochemical reactions are started by **light** — this reaction requires **ultraviolet light** in particular to get going.

2) A hydrogen atom is **substituted** (replaced) by chlorine or bromine. This is a **free-radical substitution reaction**.

Chlorine and **methane** react with a bit of a bang to form **chloromethane**:

$$CH_4 + Cl_2 \xrightarrow{UV} CH_3Cl + HCl$$

The **reaction mechanism** has three stages:

Hallo Jen. / Go away Nigel.

Initiation reactions — free radicals are produced.

1) Sunlight provides enough energy to break the Cl-Cl bond — this is **photodissociation**.
$$Cl_2 \xrightarrow{UV} 2Cl\cdot$$
2) The bond splits **equally** and each atom gets to keep one electron — **homolytic fission**. The atom becomes a highly reactive **free radical**, $Cl\cdot$, because of its **unpaired electron**.

Propagation reactions — free radicals are used up and created in a chain reaction.

1) $Cl\cdot$ attacks a **methane** molecule: $Cl\cdot + CH_4 \rightarrow \cdot CH_3 + HCl$

2) The new **methyl free radical**, $\cdot CH_3$, can attack another Cl_2 molecule: $\cdot CH_3 + Cl_2 \rightarrow CH_3Cl + Cl\cdot$

3) The new $Cl\cdot$ can attack **another** CH_4 molecule, and so on, until all the Cl_2 or CH_4 molecules are wiped out.

Termination reactions — free radicals are mopped up.
1) If two free radicals join together, they make a **stable molecule**.
2) There are **heaps** of possible termination reactions.
Here are a couple of them to give you the idea: $Cl\cdot + \cdot CH_3 \rightarrow CH_3Cl$
$\cdot CH_3 + \cdot CH_3 \rightarrow C_2H_6$

Some products formed will be trace impurities in the final sample.

The reaction between bromine and methane works in exactly the same way.
$$CH_4 + Br_2 \xrightarrow{UV} CH_3Br + HBr$$

Alkanes — Substitution Reactions

The Problem is — You End Up With a Mixture of Products

1) The big problem with free-radical substitution is that you **don't only get chloromethane**, but a **mixture of products**.

2) If there's **too much chlorine** in the reaction mixture, some of the remaining **hydrogen atoms** on the **chloromethane molecule** will be swapped for chlorine atoms.

   The propagation reactions happen again, this time to make **dichloromethane**.

   $$Cl^{\bullet} + CH_3Cl \rightarrow CH_2Cl^{\bullet} + HCl$$

   $$CH_2Cl^{\bullet} + Cl_2 \rightarrow \textbf{CH}_2\textbf{Cl}_2 + Cl^{\bullet}$$
   $$\textbf{dichloromethane}$$

3) It doesn't stop there. Another substitution reaction can take place to form **trichloromethane**.

   $$Cl^{\bullet} + CH_2Cl_2 \rightarrow CHCl_2^{\bullet} + HCl$$

   $$CHCl_2^{\bullet} + Cl_2 \rightarrow \textbf{CHCl}_3 + Cl^{\bullet}$$
   $$\textbf{trichloromethane}$$

4) **Tetrachloromethane** (CCl_4) is formed in the last possible substitution. There are no more hydrogens attached to the carbon atom, so the substitution process has to stop.

5) So the end product is a mixture of CH_3Cl, CH_2Cl_2, $CHCl_3$ and CCl_4. This is a nuisance, because you have to separate the **chloromethane** from the other three unwanted by-products.

6) The best way of reducing the chance of these by-products forming is to have an **excess of methane**. This means there's a greater chance of a chlorine radical colliding only with a **methane molecule** and not a **chloromethane molecule**.

Practice Questions

Q1 What's a free radical?

Q2 What's homolytic fission?

Q3 What's photodissociation?

Q4 Complete this equation: $CH_4 + Cl_2 \xrightarrow{UV}$

Q5 Write down three possible products, other than chloromethane, from the photochemical reaction between CH_4 and Cl_2.

Exam Questions

Q1 When irradiated with UV light, methane gas will react with bromine to form a mixture of several organic compounds.

(a) Name the type of mechanism involved in this reaction. [1 mark]

(b) Write an overall equation to show the formation of bromomethane from methane and bromine. [1 mark]

(c) Write down the two equations in the propagation step for the formation of CH_3Br. [2 marks]

(d) (i) Explain why a tiny amount of ethane is found in the product mixture. [1 mark]
   (ii) Name the mechanistic step that leads to the formation of ethane. [1 mark]
   (iii) Write the equation for the formation of ethane in this reaction. [1 mark]

(e) Name the major product formed when a large excess of bromine reacts with methane in the presence of UV light. [1 mark]

Q2 The alkane ethane is a saturated hydrocarbon. It is mostly unreactive, but will react with bromine in a photochemical reaction.

Write an equation and outline the mechanism for the photochemical reaction of bromine with ethane. You should assume ethane is in excess. [6 marks]

This page is like... totally radical, man...

Mechanisms can be an absolute pain in the bum to learn, but unfortunately reactions are what Chemistry's all about. If you don't like it, you should have taken art — no mechanisms in that, just pretty pictures. Ah well, there's no going back now. You've just got to sit down and learn the stuff. Keep hacking away at it, till you know it all off by heart.

Alkenes and Polymers

Alkenes are short. But join lots of them together and you get polymers, which are very long. That's these pages in a nutshell.

Alkenes are **Unsaturated Hydrocarbons**

1) Alkenes have the **general formula C_nH_{2n}**. They're just made of carbon and hydrogen atoms, so they're **hydrocarbons**.

2) Alkene molecules **all** have at least one **C=C double covalent bond**. Molecules with C=C double bonds are **unsaturated** because they can make more bonds with extra atoms in **addition** reactions.

   Here are a few pretty **alkenes**:

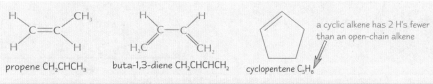

propene CH_2CHCH_3 buta-1,3-diene $CH_2CHCHCH_2$ cyclopentene C_5H_8

a cyclic alkene has 2 H's fewer than an open-chain alkene

A **Double Bond** is made up of a **Sigma (σ) Bond** and a **Pi (π) Bond**

1) A σ **bond** (sigma bond) is formed when two **s orbitals overlap** (look at page 22 if you've forgotten what an s orbital is).

2) The two s orbitals overlap in a straight line — this gives the **highest possible electron density** between the two nuclei. This is a **single** covalent bond.

1) A π **bond** is formed when two **p orbitals** overlap.

2) It's got **two parts** to it — one 'above' and one 'below' the molecular axis. This is because the π orbitals which overlap are **dumb-bell shaped** (see page 22 if you're bewildered).

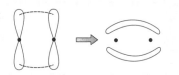

Alkenes are **Much More Reactive** than Alkanes

1) Each **double bond** in an alkene is a bit like a hot dog. The π **bond** is the bun and the σ **bond** is sandwiched in the middle like the sausage.

2) Because there's two pairs of electrons in the bond, the C=C double bond has a really **high electron density**. This makes alkenes pretty reactive.

3) Another reason for the high reactivity is that the π **bond** sticks out above and below the rest of the molecule. So, the π **bond** is likely to be attacked by **electrophiles** (see p66).

4) Because the double bond's so **reactive**, alkenes are handy **starting points** for making other organic compounds and for making **petrochemicals**.

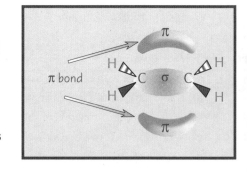

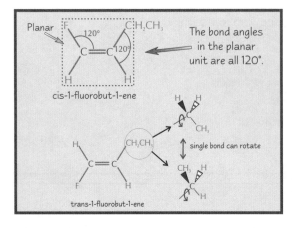

cis-1-fluorobut-1-ene

The bond angles in the planar unit are all 120°.

single bond can rotate

trans-1-fluorobut-1-ene

Double Bonds Can't **Rotate**

1) The carbon atoms in the C=C double bond can't **rotate**. This is because the p orbitals have to **overlap** to form a π **bond**. The C=C double bond and the atoms bonded to these carbons are **planar** (flat) and **rigid** (they can't bend or twist much).

2) Ethene, C_2H_2, is completely planar, but in larger alkenes, only the >C=C< unit is planar — atoms can still rotate around other **single bonds** within the molecule.

3) The **restricted rotation** around the C=C double bond is what causes **cis-trans** or **E/Z isomerism** (see p51).

Alkenes and Polymers

Alkenes *Join Up* to form *Addition Polymers*

1) The **double bonds** in alkenes can open up and join together to make long chains called **polymers**. It's kind of like they're holding hands in a big line. The individual, small alkenes are called **monomers**.

2) This is called **addition polymerisation**. For example, **poly(ethene)** is made by the **addition polymerisation** of **ethene**.

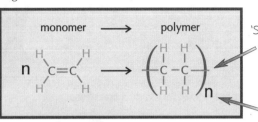

'Side-links' show that both sides are attached to other units.

The bit in brackets is the 'repeat unit' (or 'repeating unit'). n represents the number of repeat units.

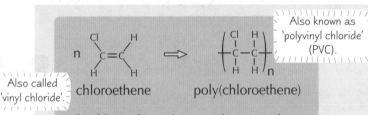

polymer
poly(propene)

repeat unit

monomer
propene

3) To find the **monomer** used to form an addition polymer, take the **repeat unit** and add a **double bond**.

Different Alkenes give Polymers with Different Properties

You can polymerise molecules other than basic alkenes:

Also known as 'polyvinyl chloride' (PVC).

Also called 'vinyl chloride'.

chloroethene   poly(chloroethene)

Poly(chloroethene) has a wide range of uses — for example, it's used to make water pipes, for insulation on electric wires and as a building material.

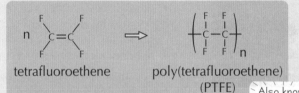

tetrafluoroethene   poly(tetrafluoroethene) (PTFE)

Also known as Teflon®

Poly(tetrafluoroethene) is chemically **inert** and has **non-stick** properties. This makes it ideal as a coating for frying pans.

Practice Questions

Q1 What is an alkene?

Q2 Describe the arrangement of electrons in a single bond and in a double bond.

Q3 What is addition polymerisation?

Exam Question

Q1 One of the most important products made from crude oil is ethene.

a) Draw diagrams to show how the orbitals interact in the bonding between the carbon atoms in ethene. [3 marks]

b) Describe the shape of an ethene molecule and explain, in terms of bonding, why it has this shape. [3 marks]

c) Explain why ethene is particularly useful to the petrochemical industry. [2 marks]

d) Chloroethene CH_2=CHCl forms the polymer poly(chloroethene), commonly known as PVC. Write an equation for the polymerisation of chloroethene, including a full structural formula showing the repeating unit in poly(chloroethene). [2 marks]

Alkenes — join up today, your polymer needs YOU...

There's a lot here, make no mistake. Some of it's kinda tricky too... that σ and π bond stuff, for example. The rest should be more straightforward — but just make <u>very sure</u> that if they give you the structure of a polymer in the exam, you could draw the monomer that it's made from (including that vital double bond). And vice versa, of course. Okay... cup of tea time.

Polymers and the Environment

Polymers are amazingly useful. But they have one big drawback...

Polymers — *Useful* but Difficult to *Get Rid Of*

1) Synthetic polymers have loads of **advantages**, so they're incredibly widespread these days — we take them pretty much for granted.

   Just imagine what you'd have to live without if there ⟹ were no polymers...

   (Okay... I could live without the polystyrene head, but the rest of this stuff is pretty useful.)

2) One of the really useful things about many everyday polymers is that they're very **unreactive**. This means food doesn't react with the PTFE coating on pans, plastic windows don't rot, plastic crates can be left out in the rain and they'll be okay, and so on.

3) But this **lack** of reactivity also leads to a **problem**.
   Most polymers aren't **biodegradable**, and so they're really difficult to **dispose of**.

4) In the UK over **2 million** tonnes of plastic waste are produced each year. It's important to find ways to get rid of this waste while minimising **environmental damage**. There are various possible approaches...

Waste Plastics can be *Buried*

1) **Landfill** is one option for dealing with waste plastics. It is generally used when the plastic is:
   - difficult to separate from other waste,
   - not in sufficient quantities to make separation financially worthwhile,
   - too difficult technically to recycle.

   Landfill means taking waste to a landfill site, compacting it, and then covering it with soil.

2) But because the **amount of waste** we generate is becoming more and more of a problem, there's a need to **reduce** landfill as much as possible.

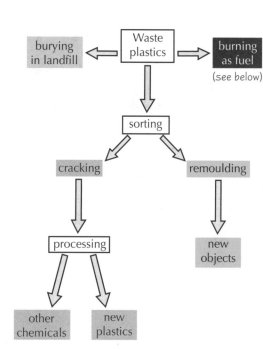

Waste Plastics can be *Recycled*

Because many plastics are made from non-renewable **oil-fractions**, it makes sense to recycle plastics as much as possible.

There's more than one way to recycle plastics.
After **sorting** into different types:

- some plastics (poly(propene), for example) can be **melted** and **remoulded**,

- some plastics can be **cracked** into **monomers**, and these can be use to make more plastics or other chemicals.

Plastic products are usually marked to make sorting easier. The different numbers show different polymers

e.g. ⟨3⟩ = PVC,   and ⟨5⟩ = poly(propene)

Waste Plastics can be *Burned*

Rex and Dirk enjoy some waist plastic.

1) If recycling isn't possible for whatever reason, waste plastics can be burned — and the heat can be used to generate **electricity**.

2) This process needs to be carefully **controlled** to reduce **toxic** gases. For example, polymers that contain **chlorine** (such as **PVC**) produce **HCl** when they're burned — this has to be removed.

3) Waste gases from the combustion are passed through **scrubbers** which can **neutralise** gases such as HCl by allowing them to react with a **base**.

Polymers and the Environment

Biodegradable Polymers *Decompose* in the *Right Conditions*

Scientists can now make **biodegradable** polymers — ones that naturally **decompose**.

1) **Biodegradable polymers** decompose pretty quickly in certain conditions — because organisms can digest them. (You might get asked about 'compostable' polymers as well as 'biodegradable' ones. These two terms mean more or less the same thing — 'compostable' just means it has to decay fairly quickly, "at the speed of compost".)

2) Biodegradable polymers can be made from materials such as **starch** (from maize and other plants) and from the hydrocarbon **isoprene** (2-methyl-1,3-butadiene). So, biodegradable polymers can be produced from **renewable** raw materials or from **oil fractions**:

> Using **renewable** raw material has several **advantages**.
> (i) Raw materials aren't going to **run out** like oil will.
> (ii) When polymers biodegrade, **carbon dioxide** (a greenhouse gas — see p92) is produced. If your polymer is **plant-based**, then the CO_2 released as it decomposes is the same CO_2 absorbed by the plant when it grew. But with an **oil-based** biodegradable polymer, you're effectively transferring carbon from the oil to the atmosphere.
> (iii) Over their 'lifetime' some plant-based polymers **save energy** compared to oil-based plastics.

But whatever raw material you use, at the moment the energy for making polymers usually comes from fossil fuels.

3) Even though they're biodegradable, these polymers still need the right conditions before they'll decompose. You **couldn't** necessarily just put them in a landfill and expect them to perish away — because there's a lack of moisture and oxygen under all that compressed soil. You need to chuck them on a big compost heap. This means that you still need to **collect** and **separate** the biodegradable polymers from non-biodegradable plastics. At the moment, they're also **more expensive** than oil-based equivalents.

4) There are various potential uses — e.g. plastic sheeting used to protect plants from the frost can be made from poly(ethene) with **starch grains** embedded in it. In time the starch is broken down by **microorganisms** and the remaining poly(ethene) crumbles into dust. There's no need to collect and dispose of the old sheeting.

Practice Questions

Q1 Many plastics are unreactive. Describe one benefit and one disadvantage of this.

Q2 Which harmful gas is produced during the combustion of PVC?

Q3 Describe three ways in which used polymers such as poly(propene) can be handled.

Q4 What is a compostable polymer? Name two things compostable polymers can be made from.

Exam Questions

Q1 Waste plastics can be disposed of by burning.
   a) Describe one advantage of disposing of waste plastics by burning. [1 mark]
   b) Describe a disadvantage of burning waste plastic that contains chlorine, and explain how the impact of this disadvantage could be reduced. [2 marks]

Q2 Describe one way in which waste poly(propene) could be recycled into new plastic objects. [2 marks]

Q3 Apart from being biodegradable, describe TWO benefits of using starch- or maize-based polymers instead of oil-based polymers. [2 marks]

Phil's my recycled plastic plane — but I don't know where to land Phil...

You might have noticed that all this recycling business is a hot topic these days. And not just in the usual places, such as Chemistry books. No, no, no... recycling even makes it regularly onto the news as well. This suits examiners just fine — they like you to know how useful and important chemistry is. So learn this stuff, pass your exam, and do some recycling.

Reactions of Alkenes

Alkenes do loads of weird and wacky stuff — but I've squished all that you need to know on this double-page spread.

Electrophilic Addition Reactions Happen to Alkenes

1) **Electrophilic addition** reactions aren't too complicated.
The **double bonds** open up and atoms are **added** to the carbon atoms.

2) Addition reactions happen because the double bond has got plenty of
electrons and is easily attacked by electrophiles.

> **Electrophiles** are **electron-pair acceptors** — they're
> usually a bit short of electrons, so they're **attracted**
> to areas where there's lots of them about.
> Here are a couple of examples of electrophiles:
> - **Positively charged ions**, like H^+, NO_2^+.
> - **Polar molecules** — the δ+ atom is attracted
>   to places with lots of electrons

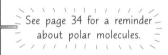
See page 34 for a reminder about polar molecules.

3) The double bond is also **nucleophilic** — it's attracted to places that don't have enough **electrons**.

Adding Hydrogen to C=C Bonds Produces Alkanes

1) Ethene will react with **hydrogen** gas to produce ethane.
It needs a **nickel catalyst** and a temperature of **150 °C** though.

$$H_2C{=}CH_2 + H_2 \xrightarrow[150\,°C]{Ni} CH_3CH_3$$

2) **Margarine's** made by 'hydrogenating' **unsaturated vegetable oils**. By removing some **double bonds**,
you raise the **melting point** of the oil so that it becomes **solid** at room temperature.

Use Bromine Water to Test for C=C Double Bonds

When you shake an alkene with **orange bromine water**, the solution quickly
decolourises. Bromine is added across the double bond to form a colourless
dibromoalkane — this happens by **electrophilic addition**.

Here's the mechanism...

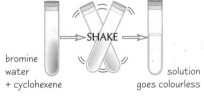

bromine water + cyclohexene → SHAKE → solution goes colourless

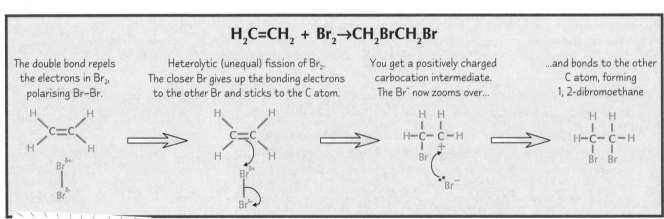

$$H_2C{=}CH_2 + Br_2 \rightarrow CH_2BrCH_2Br$$

| The double bond repels the electrons in Br_2, polarising Br–Br. | Heterolytic (unequal) fission of Br_2. The closer Br gives up the bonding electrons to the other Br and sticks to the C atom. | You get a positively charged carbocation intermediate. The Br^- now zooms over... | ...and bonds to the other C atom, forming 1, 2-dibromoethane |

Chlorine and iodine do this with alkenes too.

A carbocation is an organic ion containing a positively charged carbon atom.

Reactions of Alkenes

Adding **Hydrogen Halides** to **Unsymmetrical Alkenes** Forms **Two Products**

1) Alkenes also undergo **electrophilic addition** reactions with HBr, to form **bromoalkanes**.

2) If the HBr adds to an **unsymmetrical** alkene, like propene, there are two possible products.

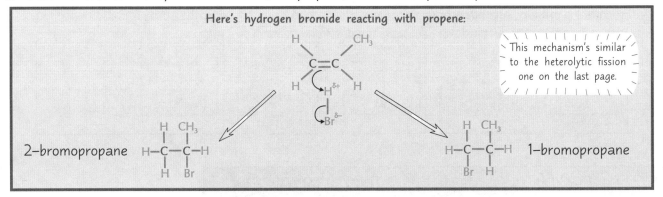

3) A symmetrical alkene, like ethene or but-2-ene, can only form one product in this type of reaction:

Ethanol is Manufactured by **Steam Hydration**

1) Ethene can be **hydrated** by **steam** at 300 °C and a pressure of 60-70 atm. It needs a solid **phosphoric(V) acid catalyst**.

2) The reaction's **reversible** and the reaction yield is low — only about 5%. This sounds rubbish, but you can **recycle** the unreacted ethene gas, making the overall yield a much more profitable **95%**.

$$H_2C=CH_{2(g)} + H_2O_{(g)} \underset{\substack{300\ °C \\ 60\ atm}}{\overset{H_3PO_4}{\rightleftharpoons}} CH_3CH_2OH_{(g)}$$

Practice Questions

Q1 What is an electrophile?

Q2 Why do alkenes react with electrophiles?

Q3 Write an equation for the hydrogenation of ethene.

Exam Question

Q1 But-1-ene is an alkene. Alkenes contain at least one C=C double bond.
  a) Describe how bromine water can be used to test for C=C double bonds. [2 marks]

  b) Name the reaction mechanism involved in the above test. [2 marks]

  c) Hydrogen bromide will react with but-1-ene by this mechanism, producing two isomeric products.
     Draw the displayed formulas of these two isomers [2 marks]

This section is free from all GM ingredients...

Mechanisms are another of those classics that examiners just love. You need to know the electrophilic addition examples on these pages, so shut the book and scribble them out. Make sure you know the tests for double bonds too. They aren't as handy in real life as, say, a tin opener, but you won't need a tin opener in the exam. Unless your exam paper comes in a tin.

Alcohols

These two pages could well be enough to put you off alcohols for life...

Alcohols are **Primary**, **Secondary** or **Tertiary**

1) The alcohol homologous series has the **general formula $C_nH_{2n+1}OH$**.

2) An alcohol is **primary**, **secondary** or **tertiary**, depending on which carbon atom the **–OH** group is bonded to...

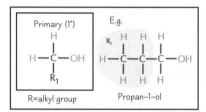
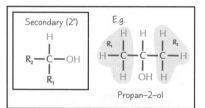
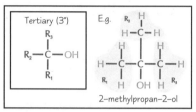

The Hydroxyl Group –OH Can Form **Hydrogen Bonds**

The **polar** –OH group on alcohols helps them to form **hydrogen bonds** (see p35), which gives them certain properties...

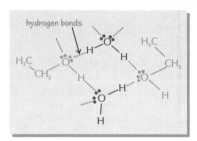

1) When you mix an alcohol with water, hydrogen bonds form between the **–OH** and H_2O. If it's a **small** alcohol (e.g. methanol, ethanol or propan-1-ol), hydrogen bonding lets it mix freely with water — it's **miscible** with water.

2) In **larger alcohols**, most of the molecule is a non-polar carbon chain, so there's less attraction for the polar H_2O molecules. This means that as alcohols **increase in size**, their miscibility in water **decreases.**

3) Hydrogen bonding is the **strongest** kind of intermolecular force, so it gives alcohols **high boiling points** compared to non-polar compounds, e.g. alkanes of similar sizes.

You might also hear it said that alcohols have relatively low volatility. Volatility is the tendency of something to evaporate into a gas.

Ethanol Can be Made by **Steam Hydration** or **Fermentation**

There are two methods of producing ethanol that you need to know about:

Steam Hydration

At the moment most industrial ethanol is produced by **steam hydration of ethene** with a **phosphoric acid catalyst** (see p67). The ethene comes from cracking heavy fractions of crude oil.

$$H_2C{=}CH_{2\,(g)} + H_2O_{(g)} \xrightleftharpoons[\substack{300\,°C \\ 60\,atm}]{H_3PO_4} CH_3CH_2OH_{(g)}$$

Fermentation

In the future, when crude oil supplies start **running out**, petrochemicals like ethene will be expensive — so producing ethanol by **fermentation** will become much more important...

Industrial Production of Ethanol by Fermentation

1) Fermentation is an **exothermic** process, carried out by **yeast** in **anaerobic conditions** (without oxygen).

2) Yeast produces an **enzyme** which converts sugars, such as glucose, into **ethanol** and **carbon dioxide**.

3) The enzyme works at an **optimum** (ideal) temperature of **30-40 °C**. If it's too cold, the reaction is **slow** — if it's too hot, the enzyme is **denatured** (damaged).

4) When the solution reaches about **15% ethanol**, the yeast dies. **Fractional distillation** is used to increase the concentration of ethanol.

5) Fermentation is **low-tech** — it uses cheap equipment and **renewable resources**. The ethanol produced by this method has to be **purified** though.

$$C_6H_{12}O_{6\,(aq)} \xrightarrow[\text{yeast}]{\text{warm}} 2C_2H_5OH_{(aq)} + 2CO_{2\,(g)}$$
glucose

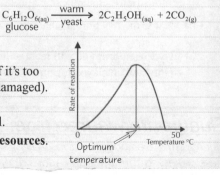

Alcohols

Alcohols Have a **Wide Variety** of Uses

1) **Ethanol** is the alcohol found in **alcoholic drinks**.
2) **Methylated spirits** is an industrial **solvent**. It's basically ethanol, with some methanol and purple dye added to make it **undrinkable** and tax-exempt. Ethanol will dissolve **polar**, **non-polar** and some **ionic compounds**.
3) Ethanol is also being used increasingly as a **fuel**, particularly in countries with few oil reserves.
4) **Unleaded petrol** contains 5% methanol and 15% MTBE (an ether made from methanol) to improve combustion.
5) Methanol is important as a **feedstock** (starting point) for manufacturing organic chemicals, e.g. plastics and dyes.

Alcohols can be **Dehydrated** to Form **Alkenes**

1) You can make ethene by **eliminating** water from **ethanol** in a **dehydration reaction**.

$$C_2H_5OH \rightarrow CH_2{=}CH_2 + H_2O$$

2) The ethanol is mixed with an **acid catalyst** and heated to **170 °C**.
3) The ethene that is produced is collected over water.
4) The acid catalyst used is either **concentrated sulfuric acid** (H_2SO_4) or **concentrated phosphoric acid** (H_3PO_4)

Reacting a **Carboxylic Acid** With **Ethanol** Produces an **Ester**

1) If you warm **ethanol** with a **carboxylic acid** (like ethanoic acid) and a **strong acid catalyst** (concentrated sulfuric acid will do), it forms an ester (**ethyl ethanoate** in this case).
2) The **O–H** bond in ethanol is broken in the **esterification** reaction.

This stuff smells of pear drops — esters generally smell fruity.

$$C_2H_5OH + CH_3COOH \rightleftharpoons CH_3C{\begin{smallmatrix}=O\\O-CH_2CH_3\end{smallmatrix}} + H_2O$$

Practice Questions

Q1 What is the general formula for an alcohol?

Q2 How do the boiling points of alcohols compare with the boiling points of similarly sized alkanes?

Q3 Give three uses of alcohols.

Exam Questions

Q1 Butanol C_4H_9OH has four chain and positional isomers. Name each isomer and class it as primary, secondary or tertiary. **[8 marks]**

a)
```
    H  H  H  H
    |  |  |  |
H – C– C– C– C–OH
    |  |  |  |
    H  H  H  H
```

b)
```
        H
        |
  H–C–H
  H  |  H
  |  |  |
H–C– C– C– H
  |  |  |
  H  OH H
```

c)
```
  H  H  H  H
  |  |  |  |
H–C– C– C– C–H
  |  |  |  |
  H  H  OH H
```

d)
```
        OH
        |
  H–C–H
  H  |  H
  |  |  |
H–C– C– C– H
  |  |  |
  H  H  H
```

[6 marks]

Q2 Ethanol is a useful alcohol.

a) State whether ethanol is a primary, secondary or tertiary alcohol, and explain why. **[2 marks]**

b) Industrially, ethanol can be produced by fermentation of glucose, $C_6H_{12}O_6$.
(i) Write a balanced equation for this reaction. **[1 mark]**
(ii) State two optimum conditions for fermentation. **[2 marks]**

c) At present most ethanol is produced by the acid-catalysed hydration of ethene. Why is this? Why might this change in the future? **[3 marks]**

Euuurghh, what a page... I think I need a drink...

Not much to learn here — a few basic definitions, some fiddly explanations of properties in terms of bonding, 4 or 5 uses, a couple of industrial processes, a dehydration reaction, an esterification reaction... Like I said, not much here at all. Think I'm going to faint. [THWACK]

Oxidation of Alcohols

Another page of alcohol reactions. Probably not what you wanted for Christmas...

The Simple way to Oxidise Alcohols is to **Burn Them**

It doesn't take much to set ethanol alight and it burns with a **pale blue flame**. The C–C and C–H bonds are broken as the ethanol is **completely oxidised** to make carbon dioxide and water. This is a **combustion** reaction.

$$C_2H_5OH_{(l)} + 3O_{2(g)} \rightarrow 2CO_{2(g)} + 3H_2O_{(g)}$$

If you burn any alcohol along with plenty of oxygen you get carbon dioxide and water as products.
But if you want to end up with something more interesting, you need a more sophisticated way of oxidising...

How Much an Alcohol can be **Oxidised** Depends on its **Structure**

You can use the **oxidising agent acidified potassium dichromate(VI)** ($K_2Cr_2O_7/H_2SO_4$) to **mildly** oxidise alcohols.

- **Primary** alcohols are oxidised to **aldehydes** and then to **carboxylic acids**.
- **Secondary** alcohols are oxidised to **ketones** only.
- **Tertiary** alcohols won't be oxidised.

The orange dichromate(VI) ion is reduced to the green chromium(III) ion, Cr^{3+}.

Aldehydes and **ketones** are **carbonyl** compounds — they have the functional group C=O.
Their general formula is $C_nH_{2n}O$.

1) **Aldehydes** have a **hydrogen** and **one alkyl group** attached to the carbonyl carbon atom.
E.g.

propanal
CH_3CH_2CHO

2) **Ketones** have **two alkyl groups** attached to the carbonyl carbon atom.
E.g.

propanone
CH_3COCH_3

Primary Alcohols will Oxidise to **Aldehydes** and **Carboxylic Acids**

$$R-CH_2-OH + [O] \longrightarrow R-C\substack{\nearrow O \\ \searrow H} + [O] \xrightarrow{reflux} R-C\substack{\nearrow O \\ \searrow OH}$$

+ H_2O

primary alcohol   aldehyde   carboxylic acid

[O] = oxidising agent

You can control how **far** the alcohol is oxidised by controlling the **reaction conditions** (see next page).

Secondary Alcohols will Oxidise to **Ketones**

$$R_1-\underset{R_2}{\overset{H}{\underset{|}{\overset{|}{C}}}}-OH + [O] \xrightarrow{reflux} \overset{R_1}{\underset{R_2}{>}}C=O + H_2O$$

1) Refluxing a secondary alcohol, e.g. propan-2-ol, with acidified dichromate(VI) will produce a **ketone**.
2) Ketones can't be oxidised easily, so even prolonged refluxing won't produce anything more.

Tertiary Alcohols can't be Oxidised Easily

Tertiary alcohols don't react with potassium dichromate(VI) at all — the solution stays orange. The only way to oxidise tertiary alcohols is by **burning** them.

Oxidation of Alcohols

Distil for an **Aldehyde**, and **Reflux** for a **Carboxylic Acid**

You can control how **far** a primary alcohol is oxidised by controlling the **reaction conditions**:

Oxidising Primary Alcohols

1) Gently heating ethanol with potassium dichromate(VI) solution and sulfuric acid in a test tube should produce "apple" smelling **ethanal** (an aldehyde). However, it's **really tricky** to control the amount of heat and the aldehyde is usually oxidised to form "vinegar" smelling **ethanoic acid**.

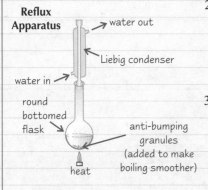

Reflux Apparatus
water out
Liebig condenser
water in
round bottomed flask
anti-bumping granules (added to make boiling smoother)
heat

2) To get just the **aldehyde**, you need to get it out of the oxidising solution **as soon** as it's formed. You can do this by gently heating excess alcohol with a **controlled** amount of oxidising agent in **distillation apparatus**, so the aldehyde (which boils at a lower temperature than the alcohol) is distilled off **immediately**.

3) To produce the **carboxylic acid**, the alcohol has to be **vigorously oxidised**. The alcohol is mixed with excess oxidising agent and heated under **reflux**. Heating under reflux means you can increase the **temperature** of an organic reaction to boiling without losing **volatile** solvents, reactants or products. Any vaporised compounds are cooled, condense and drip back into the reaction mixture. Handy, hey?

Practice Questions

Q1 What's the difference between an aldehyde and a ketone?

Q2 What will acidified potassium dichromate(VI) oxidise secondary alcohols to?

Q3 What is the colour change when potassium dichromate(VI) is reduced?

Q4 Why are anti-bumping granules used in distillation and reflux?

Exam Question

Q1 A student wanted to produce the aldehyde propanal from propanol, and set up reflux apparatus using acidified potassium dichromate(VI) as the oxidising agent.

  a) Draw a labelled diagram of reflux apparatus. Explain why reflux apparatus is arranged in this way.   [2 marks]

  b) The student tested his product and found that he had not produced propanal.
    (i) What is the student's product?   [1 mark]
    (ii) Write equations to show the two-stage reaction. You may use [O] to represent the oxidising agent.   [2 marks]
    (iii) What technique should the student have used and why?   [2 marks]

  c) The student also tried to oxidise 2-methylpropan-2-ol, unsuccessfully.
    (i) Draw the full structural formula for 2-methylpropan-2-ol.   [1 mark]
    (ii) Why is it not possible to oxidise 2-methylpropan-2-ol with an oxidising agent?   [1 mark]

I.... I .... just can't do it, R2...

Don't give up now. Only as a fully-trained Chemistry Jedi, with the force as your ally, can you take on the Examiner. If you quit now, if you choose the easy path as Wader did, all the marks you've fought for will be lost. Be strong. Don't give in to hate — that leads to the dark side...   (Only a few more pages to go before you're done with this section...)

Halogenoalkanes

*If you haven't had enough of organic chemistry yet, there's more. If you **have** had enough — there's still more.*

Halogenoalkanes are Alkanes with Halogen Atoms

A **halogenoalkane** is an alkane with at least one **halogen atom** in place of a hydrogen atom.

E.g.

trichloromethane

2-iodopropane

2-bromo-2-chloro-1, 1, 1-trifluoroethane

CFCs are Halogenoalkanes

1) **Chlorofluorocarbons** (**CFCs**) are well-known halogenoalkanes.

2) They contain only chlorine, fluorine and carbon — all the hydrogens have been replaced.

trichlorofluoromethane

chlorotrifluoromethane

3) They're very **stable**, **volatile**, **non-flammable** and **non-toxic**. They were used a lot — e.g. in **fridges**, **aerosol cans**, **dry cleaning** and **air-conditioning** — until scientists realised they were destroying the **ozone layer**. See page 94 for more about the ozone layer.

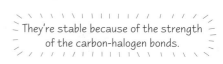
They're stable because of the strength of the carbon-halogen bonds.

Chemists Developed Alternatives to CFCs

1) The **Montreal Protocol** of 1989 was an **international treaty** to phase out the use of CFCs and other ozone-destroying halogenoalkanes by the year 2000. There were a few **permitted uses** such as in medical inhalers and in fire extinguishers used in submarines.

2) Scientists supported the treaty, and worked on finding **alternatives** to CFCs.

- **HCFCs (hydrochlorofluorocarbons)** and **HFCs (hydrofluorocarbons)** are being used as temporary alternatives to CFCs until safer products are developed. **Hydrocarbons** are also used.

- **HCFCs** are broken down in the atmosphere in 10-20 years. They still damage the ozone layer, but their effect is much smaller than CFCs.

- **HFCs** are broken down in the atmosphere too **and** they don't contain chlorine, so they don't affect the ozone layer.

- Unfortunately, **HFCs and HCFCs are greenhouse gases** — they're 1000 times worse than carbon dioxide.

- Some **hydrocarbons** are being used in fridges but these are greenhouse gases too.

- Nowadays, most aerosols have been replaced by **pump spray systems** or use **nitrogen** as the propellant. Many industrial fridges and freezers now use **ammonia** as the coolant gas, and **carbon dioxide** is used to make foamed polymers.

These substances do have **drawbacks**, but they're currently the **least environmentally damaging** of all the alternatives.

3) The ozone holes **still** form in the spring but the **rate of decrease** of ozone is **slowing** — so things are looking up.

Halogenoalkanes

PVC and PTFE are (Polymer) Halogenoalkanes

The plastics PVC and PTFE are halogenoalkanes.
Look back at page 63 and make sure you know how they're made, and some of their uses.

The Carbon–Halogen Bond in Halogenoalkanes is Polar

1) Halogens are much more **electronegative** than carbon.
   So, the **carbon–halogen bond** is **polar**.

2) The **δ+ carbon** doesn't have enough electrons.
   This means it can be attacked by a **nucleophile**.
   A nucleophile's an **electron-rich** ion or molecule.
   It donates an **electron pair** to somewhere without enough electrons.

3) **OH⁻**, **CN⁻** and **NH₃** are all **nucleophiles** which react with halogenoalkanes.
   Water's a nucleophile too, but it reacts slowly.

$$-\overset{|}{\underset{|}{C}}\overset{\delta+}{-}\overset{\delta-}{Br}$$

Halogenoalkanes can be Hydrolysed to make Alcohols

Bromoethane can be **hydrolysed** to **ethanol**.
You have to use **warm aqueous sodium** or **potassium hydroxide** or it won't work.

> Hydrolysis is when water breaks bonds.

$$CH_3CH_2Br + OH^- \xrightarrow[\text{reflux}]{OH^-/H_2O} C_2H_5OH + Br^-$$

If you don't know what 'reflux' is check out page 71.

Here's what happens. It's a nice simple **one-step mechanism**.

> This is a nucleophilic substitution reaction.

1) OH⁻ is the **nucleophile** which provides a **pair of electrons** for the $C^{\delta+}$.

2) The C-Br bond breaks **heterolytically** — **both** electrons from the bond are taken by **Br⁻**.

3) **Br⁻** falls off as **OH⁻** bonds to the carbon.

Iodoalkanes are Hydrolysed the Fastest

1) How quickly different halogenoalkanes are hydrolysed depends on **bond enthalpy** — see p80 for more on this.

2) **Weaker** carbon-halogen bonds **break** more easily — so they react **faster**.

3) **Iodoalkanes** have the **weakest bonds**, so they hydrolyse the **fastest**.

4) **Fluoroalkanes** have the **strongest bonds**, so they're the **slowest** at hydrolysing.

bond	bond enthalpy kJ mol⁻¹
C–F	467
C–Cl	346
C–Br	290
C–I	228

Faster hydrolysis as bond enthalpy decreases (the bonds are getting weaker).

Halogenoalkanes

Use **Silver Nitrate** to Compare **Reaction Rates** of *Halogenoalkanes*

1) When you mix a **halogenoalkane** with water, it reacts to form an **alcohol**.

$$R{-}X + 2H_2O \rightarrow R{-}OH + H_3O^+ + X^-$$

H$_2$O is the nucleophile.

R–X represents the halogenoalkane — the R stands for the alkyl group, the X is the halogen.

2) If you put **silver nitrate solution** in the mixture too, the silver ions react with the **halide ions** as soon as they form, giving a **silver halide precipitate** (see page 45).

$$Ag^+_{(aq)} + X^-_{(aq)} \rightarrow AgX_{(s)}$$

3) To compare the reactivities, set up four flasks each containing a different halogenoalkane, ethanol (as a solvent) and dilute silver nitrate solution.

You need to use an iodoalkane, a bromoalkane, a chloroalkane and a fluoroalkane. They should be the same in all other respects to make it a fair test.

4) You can 'measure' the rates of the reactions by timing how quickly each silver halide is **precipitated**, using the good old 'timing how long it takes the cross to disappear method' (not its official name).
To do this, stick a piece of paper with a **cross** on it under each flask and measure how long it takes until you can't see the cross any more.

5) If all the **conditions** are the same (including the temperature, concentration of reactants, etc) then you'll find that **iodoalkanes** react really quickly, **bromoalkanes** are a bit slower, and **chloroalkanes** take absolutely ages to react. **Fluoroalkanes** usually don't react at all.

If you don't like that method, here's an alternative way to get silver halide precipitates from your halogenoalkanes:

1) Warm **aqueous NaOH** with the **halogenoalkanes**. The **OH⁻ ion** acts as the nucleophile (as on the previous page).

2) Add dilute **nitric acid** to **neutralise** any spare OH⁻ ions **before** adding the **silver nitrate** solution (or else the silver nitrate will react with the OH⁻ ions to form a silver oxide precipitate, which messes up your results).

Practice Questions

Q1 What is a nucleophile?

Q2 Why is the carbon-halogen bond polar?

Q3 Why does iodoethane react faster than chloro- or bromoethane with warm, aqueous sodium hydroxide?

Q4 Give two examples of polymer halogenoalkanes.

Exam Questions

Q1 Freon-11 (trichlorofluoromethane) is a compound that was used for many years in fridges.
Its use is now banned along with other similar compounds.

   a) What name is given to this type of halogenoalkane?   [1 mark]

   b) Give three properties that these compounds have that makes them very useful.   [3 marks]

Q2 The halogenoalkane chloromethane is a substance that was formerly used as a refrigerant.

   a) Draw the structure of this molecule.   [1 mark]

   b) Give the mechanism for the hydrolysis of this molecule by warm sodium hydroxide solution.   [3 marks]

   c) What would be observed if silver nitrate solution was added to the products of the reaction in part b)?   [2 marks]

   d) What difference would you expect in the rate of hydrolysis
     in part b) if you used iodomethane instead of chloromethane?   [1 mark]

Polar bonds are like premium bonds, but are only bought by penguins...

Polar bonds get in just about every area of Chemistry. If you still think they're something to do with either bears or mints, you need to flick back to Unit 1: Section 2 and have a good read of page 34. Make sure you learn the stuff about CFCs and that hole in the ozone layer — it's always coming up in exams. Ruin the examiner's day and get it right.

Analytical Techniques

If you've got some stuff and don't know what it is, don't taste it. Stick it in an infrared spectrometer or a mass spectrometer instead. You'll wind up with some scary looking graphs. But just learn the basics, and you'll be fine.

Infrared Spectroscopy Helps You Identify Organic Molecules

1) In infrared (IR) spectroscopy, a beam of **IR radiation** is passed through a sample of a chemical.

2) The IR radiation is absorbed by the **covalent bonds** in the molecules, increasing their **vibrational** energy.

3) **Bonds between different atoms** absorb **different frequencies** of IR radiation. Bonds in different **places** in a molecule absorb different frequencies too — so the O–H group in an **alcohol** and the O–H in a **carboxylic acid** absorb different frequencies.

This table shows what **frequencies** different bonds absorb:

This tells you what the peak on the graph will look like.

Functional group	Where it's found	Frequency/ Wavenumber (cm⁻¹)	Type of absorption
C–H	most organic molecules	2800 - 3100	strong, sharp
O–H	alcohols	3200 - 3550	strong, broad
O–H	carboxylic acids	2500 - 3300	medium, broad
C=O	aldehydes, ketones, carboxylic acids	1680 - 1750	strong, sharp

You don't need to learn this data, but you do need to understand how to use it.

4) An infrared spectrometer produces a **graph** that shows you what frequencies of radiation the molecules are absorbing. You can use it to identify the **functional groups** in a molecule:

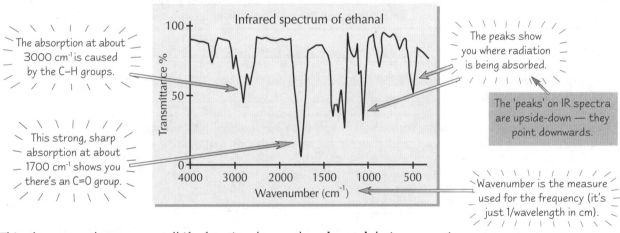

The absorption at about 3000 cm⁻¹ is caused by the C–H groups.

This strong, sharp absorption at about 1700 cm⁻¹ shows you there's an C=O group.

The peaks show you where radiation is being absorbed.

The 'peaks' on IR spectra are upside-down — they point downwards.

Wavenumber is the measure used for the frequency (it's just 1/wavelength in cm).

This also means that you can tell if a functional group has **changed** during a reaction. For example, if you **oxidise** an **alcohol** to an **aldehyde** you'll see the O–H absorption **disappear** from the spectrum, and a C=O absorption **appear**.

Infrared Spectroscopy Helps Catch Drunk Drivers

1) If a person's suspected of drink driving, they're **breathalysed**.

2) First a very quick test is done by the roadside — if it says that the driver's over the limit, they're taken into a police station for a more **accurate test** using **infrared spectroscopy**.

3) The **amount** of **ethanol vapour** in the driver's breath is found by measuring the **intensity** of the peak corresponding to the **C–H** bond in the IR spectrum. It's chosen because it's **not affected** by any **water vapour** in the breath.

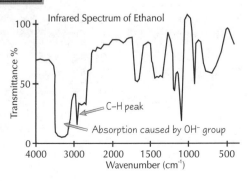

C–H peak

Absorption caused by OH⁻ group

Analytical Techniques

Mass Spectrometry Can Help to Identify Compounds

1) You saw on page 8 how you can use a mass spectrum showing the relative isotopic abundances of an element to work out its relative atomic mass. You need to make sure you can remember how to do this. You can also get mass spectra for **molecular samples**.

2) A mass spectrum is produced by a mass spectrometer. The molecules in the sample are bombarded with electrons and a **molecular ion**, $M^+_{(g)'}$ is formed when the bombarding electrons remove an electron from the molecule.

3) To find the relative molecular mass of a compound you look at the **molecular ion peak** (the **M peak**). The mass/charge value of the molecular ion peak is the **molecular mass**. ← *Assuming the ion has a 1+ charge, which it normally will have.*

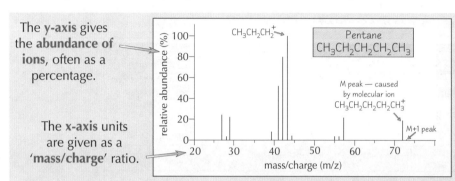

The **y-axis** gives the **abundance of ions**, often as a percentage.

The **x-axis** units are given as a 'mass/charge' ratio.

Here's the mass spectrum of pentane. Its M peak is at 72 — so the compound's M_r is 72.

For most <u>organic compounds</u> the M peak is the one with the second highest mass/charge ratio.
The smaller peak to the right of the M peak is called the M+1 peak — it's caused by the presence of the carbon isotope ^{13}C (you don't need to worry about this at AS).

The Molecular Ion can be Broken into Smaller Fragments

The bombarding electrons make some of the molecular ions break up into **fragments**.
The fragments that are ions show up on the mass spectrum, making a **fragmentation pattern**. Fragmentation patterns are actually pretty cool because you can use them to identify **molecules** and even their **structure**.

For propane, the molecular ion is $CH_3CH_2CH_3^+$, and the fragments it breaks into include CH_3^+ ($M_r = 15$) and $CH_3CH_2^+$ ($M_r = 29$).
Only the **ions** show up on the mass spectrum — the **free radicals** are 'lost'.

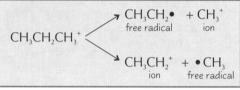

To work out the structural formula, you've got to work out what **ion** could have made each peak from its **m/z value**. (You assume that the m/z value of a peak matches the **mass** of the ion that made it.)

Example: Use this mass spectrum to work out the structure of the molecule:

It's only the m/z values you're interested in — ignore the heights of the bars.

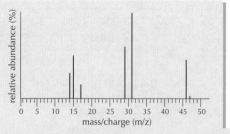

Fragment	Molecular Mass
CH_3	15
C_2H_5	29
C_3H_7	43
OH	17

1. Identify the fragments

This molecule's got a peak at 15 m/z, so it's likely to have a **CH$_3$ group**.

It's also got a peak at 17 m/z, so it's likely to have an **OH group**.

Other ions are matched to the peaks here:

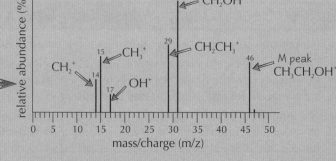

2. Piece them together to form a molecule with the correct M_r

Ethanol has all the fragments on this spectrum.

Ethanol's **molecular mass** is 46.
This should be the same as the m/z value of the M peak — it is.

Analytical Techniques

Mass Spectrometry is Used to Differentiate Between Similar Molecules

1) Even if two **different compounds** contain **the same atoms**, you can still tell them apart with mass spectrometry because they won't produce exactly the same set of fragments.

2) The formulas of **propanal** and **propanone** are shown on the right. They've got the same M_r, but different structures, so they produce some **different fragments**. For example, propanal will have a C_2H_5 fragment but propanone won't.

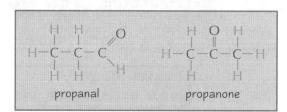

propanal   propanone

3) Every compound produces a different mass spectrum — so the spectrum's like a **fingerprint** for the compound. Large computer **databases** of mass spectra can be used to identify a compound from its spectrum.

Mass Spectrometry Has Many Uses

Mass spectrometry is actually used by scientists out there in the real world. Here are a couple of examples.

1) **Probes to Mars** have carried small mass spectrometers to study the composition of the surface of Mars and to look for molecules that might suggest that life existed on the planet.

A massage spectrum

2) Mass spectrometry can also be used to measure the **levels of pollutants** present in the environment, e.g. the amount of lead or pesticides entering the food chain via vegetables.

Practice Questions

Q1 Which parts of a molecule absorb infrared energy?

Q2 Why do most infrared spectra of organic molecules have a strong, sharp peak at around 3000 cm^{-1}?

Q3 What is meant by the molecular ion?

Q4 What is the M peak?

Q5 Give two uses of mass spectrometry.

Exam Questions

Q1 A molecule with a molecular mass of 74 produces the IR spectrum shown on the right.

Use the infrared absorption data on p75.

a) Which functional groups are responsible for peaks A and B?   [2 marks]

b) Give the molecular formula and name of this molecule. Explain your answer.   [3 marks]

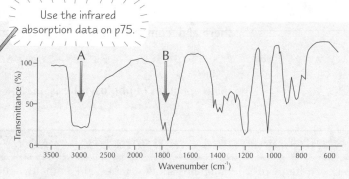

Q2 Below is the mass spectrum of an organic compound, Q.

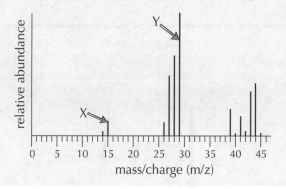

a) What is the M_r of compound Q?   [1 mark]

b) What fragments are the peaks marked X and Y most likely to correspond to?   [2 marks]

c) Suggest a structure for this compound.   [1 mark]

d) Why is it unlikely that this compound is an alcohol?   [2 marks]

Use the clues, identify a molecule — mass spectrometry my dear Watson...

Luckily you don't have to remember what any of the infrared spectrum graphs look like. But you need to be able to interpret them — they're bound to turn up in the exam. It's handy if you can learn the molecular masses of the common mass spec fragments, but if you forget them, you can work them out from the relative atomic masses of the atoms in each fragment.

Enthalpy Changes

A whole new section to enjoy — but don't forget, Big Brother is watching...

Chemical Reactions Often Have Enthalpy Changes

When chemical reactions happen, some bonds are **broken** and some bonds are **made**. More often than not, this'll cause a **change in energy**. The souped-up chemistry term for this is **enthalpy change** —

> **Enthalpy change**, ΔH (delta H), is the heat energy transferred in a reaction at **constant pressure**. The units of ΔH are **kJ mol^{-1}**.

You write $\Delta H^{\ominus}$ to show that the elements were in their **standard states** (i.e. their states at a pressure of 100 kPa), and that the measurements were made under **standard conditions**. Standard conditions are **100 kPa (about 1 atm) pressure** and a temperature of **298 K** (25 °C). The next page explains why this is necessary.

Reactions can be either Exothermic or Endothermic

> **Exothermic** reactions **give out** energy. ΔH is **negative**.

In exothermic reactions, the temperature often goes **up**.

Oxidation is exothermic. Here are 2 examples:

- The **combustion** of a fuel like methane $\longrightarrow$ $CH_{4(g)} + 2O_{2(g)} \longrightarrow CO_{2(g)} + 2H_2O_{(l)}$ $\Delta H_c^{\ominus} = -890$ kJ mol^{-1} **exothermic**

- The oxidation of **carbohydrates**, such as glucose, $C_6H_{12}O_6$, in respiration.

The symbols $\Delta H_c^{\ominus}$ and $\Delta H_r^{\ominus}$ (below) are explained on the next page.

> **Endothermic** reactions **absorb** energy. ΔH is **positive**.

In these reactions, the temperature often **falls**.

The **thermal decomposition** of calcium carbonate is endothermic.

$$CaCO_{3(s)} \longrightarrow CaO_{(s)} + CO_{2(g)} \quad \Delta H_r^{\ominus} = +178 \text{ kJ mol}^{-1} \text{ endothermic}$$

The main reactions of **photosynthesis** are also endothermic — sunlight supplies the energy.

Enthalpy Profile Diagrams Show Energy Change in Reactions

1) **Enthalpy profile diagrams** show you how the enthalpy (energy) changes during reactions.

2) The **activation energy**, E_a, is the minimum amount of energy needed to begin breaking reactant bonds and start a chemical reaction.

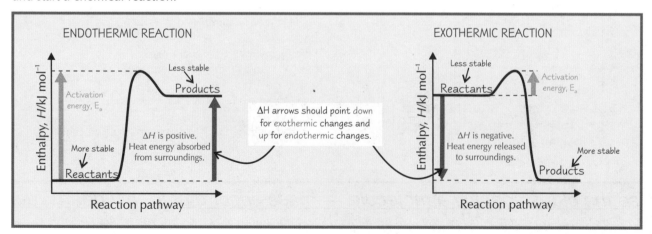

3) The **less enthalpy** a substance has, the **more stable** it is.

Enthalpy Changes

You Need to Specify the Conditions for Enthalpy Changes

1) You can't directly measure the **actual** enthalpy of a system. In practice, that doesn't matter, because it's only ever **enthalpy change** that matters. You can find enthalpy changes either by **experiment** or in **textbooks**.

2) Enthalpy changes you find in textbooks are usually **standard** enthalpy changes — enthalpy changes under **standard conditions** (**298 K** and **100 kPa**).

3) This is important because changes in enthalpy are affected by **temperature** and **pressure** — using standard conditions means that everyone can know **exactly** what the enthalpy change is describing.

There are Different Types of ΔH Depending On the Reaction

1) **Standard enthalpy change of reaction**, $\Delta H_r^\ominus$, is the enthalpy change when the reaction occurs in the **molar quantities** shown in the **chemical equation**, under standard conditions in their standard states.

2) **Standard enthalpy change of formation**, $\Delta H_f^\ominus$, is the enthalpy change when **1 mole** of a **compound** is formed from its **elements** in their standard states under standard conditions, e.g. $2C_{(s)} + 3H_{2(g)} + \frac{1}{2}O_{2(g)} \longrightarrow C_2H_5OH_{(l)}$

3) **Standard enthalpy change of combustion**, $\Delta H_c^\ominus$, is the enthalpy change when **1 mole** of a substance is completely **burned in oxygen** under standard conditions.

Practice Questions

Q1 Explain the terms exothermic and endothermic, giving an example reaction in each case.

Q2 Draw and label enthalpy profile diagrams for an exothermic and an endothermic reaction.

Q3 Define standard enthalpy of formation and standard enthalpy of combustion.

Exam Questions

Q1 Hydrogen peroxide, H_2O_2, can decompose into water and oxygen. $2H_2O_{2(l)} \longrightarrow 2H_2O_{(l)} + O_{2(g)}$ $\Delta H_r^\ominus = -98$ kJ mol^{-1}

Draw an enthalpy profile diagram for this reaction. Mark on the activation energy and ΔH. [3 marks]

Q2 Methanol, CH_3OH, when blended with petrol, can be used as a fuel. $\Delta H_c^\ominus[CH_3OH] = -726$ kJ mol^{-1}.
a) Write an equation, including state symbols, for the standard enthalpy change of combustion of methanol. [2 marks]

b) Write an equation, including state symbols, for the standard enthalpy change of formation of methanol. [2 marks]

c) Liquid petroleum gas is a fuel that contains propane, C_3H_8. Give two reasons why the following equation does not represent a standard enthalpy change of combustion. [2 marks]

$$2C_3H_{8(g)} + 10O_{2(g)} \rightarrow 8H_2O_{(g)} + 6CO_{2(g)} \qquad \Delta H_r = -4113 \text{ kJ mol}^{-1}$$

Q3 Coal is mainly carbon. It is burned as a fuel. $\Delta H_c^\ominus = -393.5$ kJ mol^{-1}

a) Write an equation, including state symbols, for the standard enthalpy change of combustion of carbon. [2 marks]

b) Explain why the standard enthalpy change of formation of carbon dioxide will also be -393.5 kJ mol^{-1} [1 mark]

c) How much energy would be released when 1 tonne of carbon is burned? (1 tonne = 1000 kg) [2 marks]

It's getting hot in here, so take off all your bonds...

Quite a few definitions here. And you need to know them all. If you're going to bother learning them, you might as well do it properly and learn all the pernickety details. They probably seem about as useful as a dead fly in your custard right now, but all will be revealed over the next few pages. Learn them now, so you've got a bit of a head start.

More on Enthalpy Changes

I bonded with my friend straight away. Now we're on the waiting list to be surgically separated.

Reactions are all about **Breaking** and **Making** Bonds

When reactions happen, **reactant bonds** are **broken** and **product bonds** are **formed**.

1) You **need** energy to break bonds, so bond breaking is **endothermic** (ΔH is **positive**).

2) Energy is **released** when bonds are formed, so this is **exothermic** (ΔH is **negative**).

3) The **enthalpy change** for a reaction is the **overall effect** of these two changes.
If you need **more** energy to **break** bonds than is released when bonds are made,
ΔH is **positive**. If it's less, ΔH is negative.

*You can only break bonds if
you've got enough energy.*

You need **Energy** to **Break** the **Attraction** between **Atoms** and **Ions**

1) In ionic bonding, **positive** and **negative ions** are attracted to each other. In covalent molecules,
the **positive nuclei** are attracted to the **negative** charge of the shared electrons in a covalent bond.

2) You need energy to **break** this attraction — **stronger** bonds take more energy to break. The **amount of energy**
you need per mole is called the **bond dissociation enthalpy**. (Of course it's got a fancy name — this is chemistry.)

3) Bond dissociation enthalpies always involve bond breaking in **gaseous compounds**. This makes comparisons fair.

Average Bond Enthalpies are *not Exact*

1) Water (H_2O) has got **two O–H bonds**.
You'd think it'd take the same amount
of energy to break them both... but it
doesn't.

> The **first** bond, H–OH$_{(g)}$: E(H–OH) = +492 kJ mol^{-1}
> The **second** bond, H–O$_{(g)}$: E(H–O) = +428 kJ mol^{-1}
> (OH$^-$ is a bit easier to break apart because of the extra electron repulsion.)
>
> So, the **average** bond enthalpy is $\dfrac{492 + 428}{2}$ = **+460 kJ mol^{-1}**.

2) The **data book** says the bond enthalpy for O–H is +463 kJ mol^{-1}. It's a bit different because it's the
average for a **much bigger range** of molecules, not just water. For example, it includes the O–H bonds
in alcohols and carboxylic acids too.

3) So when you look up an **average bond enthalpy**, what you get is:

the energy needed to break one mole of bonds in the gas phase, averaged over many different compounds

You can find out **Enthalpy Changes** in the Lab

1) To measure the **enthalpy change** for a reaction you only need to know **two things** —
   • the **number of moles** of the stuff that's reacting,
   • the change in **temperature**.

2) How you go about doing the experiment depends on what type of reaction it is.

3)
   • To find the enthalpy of **combustion** of a
   flammable liquid, you burn it — using apparatus like this...

   • As the fuel burns, it heats the water. You can work out the **heat
   absorbed** by the water if you know the **mass of water**, the
   temperature change of the water (ΔT), and the **specific heat capacity
   of water** (= 4.18 J g^{-1} K^{-1}). See the next page for all the details.

   • Ideally all the heat
   given out by the fuel
   as it burns would be
   absorbed by the
   water — allowing

   > The **specific heat capacity** of a substance is
   > the amount of heat energy it takes to raise the
   > temperature of 1 g of that substance by 1 K.

   you to work out the enthalpy change of combustion (see the next page).
   In practice though, you **always** lose some heat (as you heat the apparatus and the surroundings).

Stirrer *Thermometer*
Water *Combustion chamber*
Air *Fuel (reactant)*

4) Calorimetry can also be used to calculate an enthalpy change for a reaction that happens **in solution**, such as
neutralisation or **displacement**. For a neutralisation reaction, combine known quantities of acid and alkali in
an insulated container, and measure the temperature change. The **heat given out** can be calculated using the
formula on the next page.

More on Enthalpy Changes

Calculate **Enthalpy Changes** Using the **Equation q = mcΔT**

It seems there's a snazzy equation for everything these days, and enthalpy change is no exception:

$q = mc\Delta T$ where, q = heat lost or gained (in joules). This is the same as the enthalpy change if the pressure is constant.
m = mass of water in the calorimeter, or solution in the insulated container (in grams)
c = specific heat capacity of water (4.18 J $g^{-1}K^{-1}$)
ΔT = the change in temperature of the water or solution

Example: In a laboratory experiment, 1.16 g of an organic liquid fuel was completely burned in oxygen.
The heat formed during this combustion raised the temperature of 100 g of water from 295.3 K to 357.8 K.
Calculate the standard enthalpy of combustion, $\Delta H_c^\ominus$, of the fuel. Its M_r is 58.

Remember — m is the mass of water, NOT the mass of fuel.

① First off, you need to calculate the **amount of heat** given out by the fuel using $q = mc\Delta T$.
$q = mc\Delta T$
$q = 100 \times 4.18 \times (357.8 - 295.3) = 26\,125$ J $= 26.125$ kJ ← *Change the amount of heat from J to kJ.*

② The standard enthalpy of combustion involves 1 mole of fuel. So next you need to find out **how many moles** of fuel produced this heat. It's back to the old $n = \dfrac{mass}{M}$ equation.
$n = \dfrac{1.16}{58} = 0.02$ moles of fuel

③ So, the heat produced by 1 mole of fuel = $\dfrac{-26.125}{0.02}$
It's negative because combustion is an exothermic reaction.
$\approx$ **-1306 kJ mol^{-1}**. This is the standard enthalpy change of combustion.

The actual $\Delta H_c^\ominus$ of this compound is -1615 kJ mol^{-1} — lots of heat has been **lost** and not measured.
For example it's likely a bit would escape through the **calorimeter** and also the fuel might not **combust completely**.

Practice Questions

Q1 Briefly describe an experiment that could be carried out to find the enthalpy change of a reaction.

Q2 Why is the enthalpy change determined in a laboratory likely to be lower than the value shown in a data book?

Q3 What equation is used to calculate the heat change in a chemical reaction?

Exam Questions

Q1 A 50 cm³ sample of 0.200 M copper(II) sulfate solution placed in a polystyrene beaker gave a temperature increase of 2.6 K when excess zinc powder was added and stirred. Calculate the enthalpy change when 1 mole of zinc reacts. Assume that the specific heat capacity for the solution is 4.18 J g^{-1}K^{-1}. Ignore the increase in volume due to the zinc.
The equation for the reaction is: $Zn_{(s)} + CuSO_{4(aq)} \rightarrow Cu_{(s)} + ZnSO_{4(aq)}$ [8 marks]

Q2 a) Explain why bond enthalpies determine whether a reaction is exothermic or endothermic. [3 marks]

b) Calculate the temperature change that should be produced when 1 kg of water is heated by burning 6 g of coal. Assume the coal is pure carbon.
[The specific heat capacity of water is 4.18 J g^{-1}K^{-1}. For carbon, $\Delta H_c^\ominus = -393.5$ kJ mol^{-1}] [4 marks]

If you can't stand the enthalpy, get out of the chemistry class...

Reactions are like pulling your Lego spaceship apart and building something new. Sometimes the bits get stuck together and you need to use loads of energy to pull 'em apart. Okay, so energy's not really released when you stick them together, but you can't have everything — and it wasn't that bad an analogy up till now. Ah, well... you'd best get on and learn this stuff.

Enthalpy Calculations

You can't always work out an enthalpy change by measuring a single temperature change. But there are other ways...

Hess's Law — the Total Enthalpy Change is **Independent** of the Route Taken

Hess's Law says that:

> The **total enthalpy change** of a reaction is always **the same**, no matter **which route** is taken.
>
>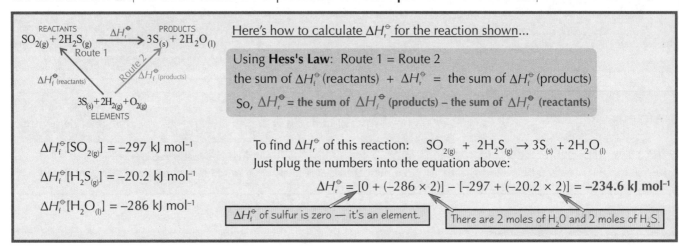
> $$2NO_{2(g)} \xrightarrow[\text{Route 1}]{\Delta H_r} N_{2(g)} + 2O_{2(g)}$$
> +114.4 kJ   Route 2   −180.8 kJ
> $$2NO_{(g)} + O_{2(g)}$$
>
> This law is handy for working out enthalpy changes that you **can't find directly** by doing an experiment.
>
> Here's an example:
> The **total enthalpy change** for route 1 is the **same** as for route 2.
> So, $\Delta H_r = +114.4 + (-180.8) = -66.4$ kJ mol⁻¹.

Enthalpy Changes Can be Worked Out From **Enthalpies of Formation**

You can find **enthalpy changes of formation** for hundreds of various compounds listed in textbooks.
They're handy because you can use them (along with Hess's Law) to find enthalpy changes for all kinds of **reactions**.

You need to know $\Delta H_f^\ominus$ for **all** the reactants and products that are **compounds**. The value of $\Delta H_f^\ominus$ for elements is **zero**.

REACTANTS
$$SO_{2(g)} + 2H_2S_{(g)} \xrightarrow{\Delta H_r^\ominus} 3S_{(s)} + 2H_2O_{(l)}$$ PRODUCTS
Route 1
$\Delta H_f^\ominus$ (reactants)   Route 2 $\Delta H_f^\ominus$ (products)
$$3S_{(s)} + 2H_{2(g)} + O_{2(g)}$$
ELEMENTS

$\Delta H_f^\ominus [SO_{2(g)}] = -297$ kJ mol⁻¹

$\Delta H_f^\ominus [H_2S_{(g)}] = -20.2$ kJ mol⁻¹

$\Delta H_f^\ominus [H_2O_{(l)}] = -286$ kJ mol⁻¹

Here's how to calculate $\Delta H_r^\ominus$ for the reaction shown...

Using **Hess's Law**: Route 1 = Route 2
the sum of $\Delta H_f^\ominus$ (reactants) + $\Delta H_r^\ominus$ = the sum of $\Delta H_f^\ominus$ (products)

So, $\Delta H_r^\ominus$ = the sum of $\Delta H_f^\ominus$ (products) − the sum of $\Delta H_f^\ominus$ (reactants)

To find $\Delta H_r^\ominus$ of this reaction: $SO_{2(g)} + 2H_2S_{(g)} \rightarrow 3S_{(s)} + 2H_2O_{(l)}$
Just plug the numbers into the equation above:

$$\Delta H_r^\ominus = [0 + (-286 \times 2)] - [-297 + (-20.2 \times 2)] = \textbf{−234.6 kJ mol⁻¹}$$

$\Delta H_f^\ominus$ of sulfur is zero — it's an element.

There are 2 moles of H_2O and 2 moles of H_2S.

It **always** works, no matter how complicated the reaction — e.g. $2NH_4NO_{3\,(s)} + C_{(s)} \rightarrow 2N_{2\,(g)} + CO_{2\,(g)} + 4H_2O_{(l)}$

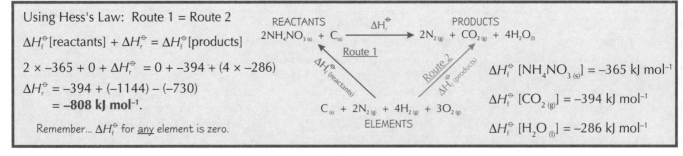

Using Hess's Law: Route 1 = Route 2

$\Delta H_f^\ominus$[reactants] + $\Delta H_r^\ominus$ = $\Delta H_f^\ominus$[products]

$2 \times -365 + 0 + \Delta H_r^\ominus = 0 + -394 + (4 \times -286)$

$\Delta H_r^\ominus = -394 + (-1144) - (-730)$
$\quad = \textbf{−808 kJ mol⁻¹}$.

Remember... $\Delta H_f^\ominus$ for <u>any</u> element is zero.

REACTANTS
$$2NH_4NO_{3\,(s)} + C_{(s)} \xrightarrow{\Delta H_r^\ominus} 2N_{2\,(g)} + CO_{2\,(g)} + 4H_2O_{(l)}$$ PRODUCTS
Route 1
$\Delta H_f^\ominus$ (reactants)   Route 2 $\Delta H_f^\ominus$ (products)
$$C_{(s)} + 2N_{2\,(g)} + 4H_{2\,(g)} + 3O_{2\,(g)}$$
ELEMENTS

$\Delta H_f^\ominus [NH_4NO_{3\,(s)}] = -365$ kJ mol⁻¹

$\Delta H_f^\ominus [CO_{2\,(g)}] = -394$ kJ mol⁻¹

$\Delta H_f^\ominus [H_2O_{(l)}] = -286$ kJ mol⁻¹

Enthalpy Changes Can Also be Found From **Enthalpies of Combustion**

You can use a similar method to find **enthalpy changes of formation** from enthalpy changes of combustion.

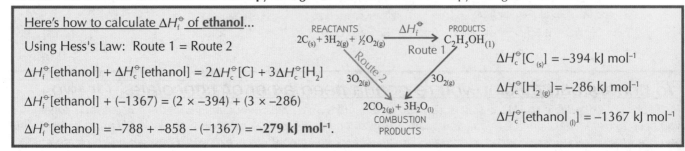

Here's how to calculate $\Delta H_f^\ominus$ of **ethanol**...

Using Hess's Law: Route 1 = Route 2

$\Delta H_f^\ominus$[ethanol] + $\Delta H_c^\ominus$[ethanol] = $2\Delta H_c^\ominus$[C] + $3\Delta H_c^\ominus$[H_2]

$\Delta H_f^\ominus$[ethanol] + (−1367) = (2 × −394) + (3 × −286)

$\Delta H_f^\ominus$[ethanol] = −788 + −858 − (−1367) = **−279 kJ mol⁻¹**.

REACTANTS
$$2C_{(s)} + 3H_{2(g)} + \tfrac{1}{2}O_{2(g)} \xrightarrow{\Delta H_f^\ominus} C_2H_5OH_{(l)}$$ PRODUCTS
Route 1
Route 2 $3O_{2(g)}$ $3O_{2(g)}$
$$2CO_{2(g)} + 3H_2O_{(l)}$$
COMBUSTION PRODUCTS

$\Delta H_c^\ominus [C_{(s)}] = -394$ kJ mol⁻¹

$\Delta H_c^\ominus [H_{2\,(g)}] = -286$ kJ mol⁻¹

$\Delta H_c^\ominus [ethanol_{(l)}] = -1367$ kJ mol⁻¹

Enthalpy Calculations

Enthalpy Changes Can Be Calculated using Average Bond Enthalpies

1) You **need** energy to break bonds, so bond breaking is an **endothermic** process (ΔH is **positive**).

2) Energy is **released** when bonds are formed, so this is an **exothermic** process (ΔH is **negative**).

3) The **enthalpy change** for a reaction is the **overall effect** of these two changes. If you need **more** energy to **break** bonds than is released when bonds are made, ΔH is **positive**. If it's **less**, ΔH is **negative**.

Enthalpy Change of Reaction	=	Total Energy Absorbed to Break Bonds	−	Total Energy Released in Making Bonds

4) **Average bond enthalpies** (the **energy needed** to **break** a bond, or the **energy given out** when a bond **forms**) are published in textbooks to help calculate **enthalpy changes** of **reactions**. They're pretty straightforward to use...

Example: Calculate the overall enthalpy change for this reaction:
$N_2 + 3H_2 \rightarrow 2NH_3$
Use the average bond enthalpy values in the table.

Bond	Average Bond Enthalpy
N≡N	945 kJ mol⁻¹
H–H	436 kJ mol⁻¹
N–H	391 kJ mol⁻¹

Bonds broken: 1 × N≡N bond broken = 1 × 945 = 945 kJ mol⁻¹
3 × H–H bonds broken = 3 × 436 = 1308 kJ mol⁻¹
Total Energy Absorbed = 945 + 1308 = **2253 kJ mol⁻¹**

Bonds formed: 6 × N–H bonds formed = 6 × 391 = 2346 kJ mol⁻¹
Total Energy Released = **2346 kJ mol⁻¹**

Enthalpy Change of Reaction = 2253 − 2346 = **−93 kJ mol⁻¹**

If you can't remember which value to subtract from which, just take the smaller number from the bigger one then add the sign at the end — positive if 'bonds broken' was the bigger number (endothermic), negative if 'bonds formed' was bigger (exothermic).

Practice Questions

Q1 What is Hess's Law?

Q2 What is the standard enthalpy change of formation of any element?

Q3 Describe how you can make a "Hess's Law triangle" to find the standard enthalpy change of a reaction using standard enthalpy changes of formation.

Exam Questions

Q1 Using the facts that the standard enthalpy change of formation of $Al_2O_{3(s)}$ is −1676 kJ mol⁻¹ and the standard enthalpy change of formation of $MgO_{(s)}$ is −602 kJ mol⁻¹, calculate the enthalpy change of the following reaction.
$Al_2O_{3(s)} + 3Mg_{(s)} \rightarrow 2Al_{(s)} + 3MgO_{(s)}$ [3 marks]

Q2 Calculate the enthalpy change for the reaction below (the fermentation of glucose).
$C_6H_{12}O_{6(s)} \rightarrow 2C_2H_5OH_{(l)} + 2CO_{2(g)}$
Use the following standard enthalpies of combustion in your calculations:
$\Delta H_c^{\ominus}$(glucose) = −2820 kJ mol⁻¹ $\Delta H_c^{\ominus}$(ethanol) = −1367 kJ mol⁻¹ [3 marks]

Q3 Calculate the standard enthalpy of formation of propane from carbon and hydrogen.
$3C_{(s)} + 4H_{2(g)} \rightarrow C_3H_{8(g)}$
Using the following data:
$\Delta H_c^{\ominus}$(propane) = −2220 kJ mol⁻¹ $\Delta H_c^{\ominus}$(carbon) = −394 kJ mol⁻¹ $\Delta H_c^{\ominus}$(hydrogen) = −286 kJ mol⁻¹ [3 marks]

Q4 The table on the right shows some average bond enthalpy values.

Bond	C–H	C=O	O=O	O–H
Average Bond Enthalpy (kJ/mol)	435	805	498	464

The complete combustion of methane can be represented by the following equation:
$CH_{4(g)} + 2O_{2(g)} \rightarrow CO_{2(g)} + 2H_2O_{(l)}$
Use the table of bond enthalpies above to calculate the enthalpy change for the reaction. [4 marks]

To understand this lot, you're gonna need a bar of chocolate. Or two...

To get your head around those Hess diagrams, you're going to have to do more than skim them. It'll also help if you know the definitions for those standard enthalpy thingumabobs. If I were you, you know what I'd do... I'd read those Hess Cycle examples again and make sure you understand how the elements/compounds at each corner were chosen to be there.

Reaction Rates

The rate of a reaction is just how quickly it happens. Lots of things can make it go faster or slower.

Particles **Must** Collide to **React**

1) Particles in liquids and gases are **always moving** and **colliding** with **each other**. They **don't** react every time though — only when the **conditions** are right. A reaction **won't** take place between two particles **unless** —

> • They collide in the **right direction**. They need to be **facing** each other the right way.
> • They collide with at least a certain **minimum** amount of kinetic (movement) **energy**.

This stuff's called **Collision Theory**.

2) The **minimum amount of kinetic energy** particles need to react is called the **activation energy**. The particles need this much energy to **break the bonds** to start the reaction.

3) Reactions with **low activation energies** often happen **pretty easily**. But reactions with **high activation energies** don't. You need to give the particles extra energy by **heating** them.

To make this a bit clearer, here's another **enthalpy profile diagram**.

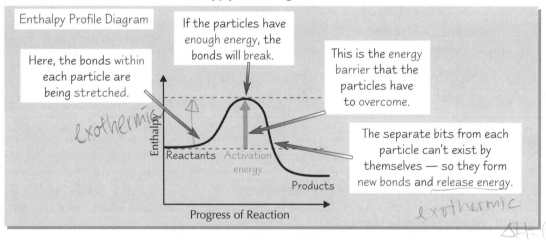

Molecules in a Gas **Don't** all have the **Same Amount of Energy**

Imagine looking down on Oxford Street when it's teeming with people. You'll see some people ambling along **slowly**, some hurrying **quickly**, but most of them will be walking with a **moderate speed**. It's the same with the **molecules** in a gas. Some **don't have much kinetic energy** and move **slowly**. Others have **loads of kinetic energy** and **whizz** along. But most molecules are somewhere **in between**.

If you plot a **graph** of the **numbers of molecules** in a gas with different **kinetic energies** you get a **Maxwell-Boltzmann distribution**. It looks like this —

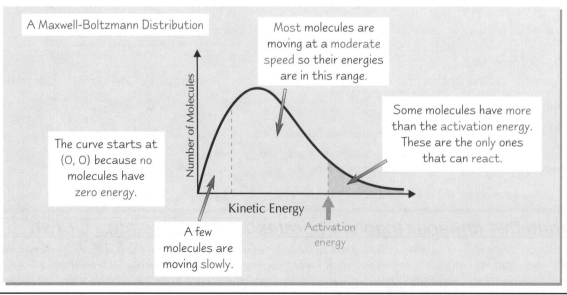

Reaction Rates

Increasing the Temperature makes Reactions Faster

1) If you increase the **temperature**, the particles will on average have more **kinetic energy** and will move **faster**.

2) So, a **greater proportion** of molecules will have more energy than the **activation energy** and be able to **react**. This changes the **shape** of the **Maxwell-Boltzmann distribution curve** — it pushes it over to the **right**.

The total number of molecules is still the same, which means the area under each curve must be the same.

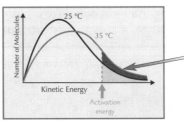

At higher temperatures, more molecules have more energy than the activation energy.

3) Because the molecules are flying about **faster**, they'll **collide more often**. This is **another reason** why increasing the temperature makes a reaction faster.

Concentration, Pressure and Catalysts also Affect the Reaction Rate

Increasing Concentration Speeds Up Reactions

If you increase the **concentration** of reactants in a **solution**, the particles will be **closer together** on average. If they're closer, they'll **collide more often**. If there are **more collisions**, they'll have **more chances** to react.

Increasing Pressure Speeds Up Reactions

If any of your reactants are **gases**, increasing the **pressure** will increase the rate of reaction. It's pretty much the same as increasing the **concentration** of a solution — at higher pressures, the particles will be **closer together**, increasing the chance of **successful collisions**.

If one of the reactants is a solid, increasing its <u>surface area</u> makes the reaction faster too.

Catalysts Can Speed Up Reactions

Catalysts are really useful. They **lower the activation energy** by providing a **different way** for the bonds to be broken and remade. If the activation energy's **lower**, more particles will have **enough energy** to react. There's heaps of information about catalysts on the next two pages.

Practice Questions

Q1 Explain the term 'activation energy'.

Q2 What is a Maxwell-Boltzmann distribution?

Q3 Name the four factors that affect the rate of a reaction.

Exam Questions

Q1 Nitrogen oxide (NO) and ozone (O_3) sometimes react to produce nitrogen dioxide (NO_2) and oxygen (O_2). How would increasing the pressure affect the rate of this reaction? Explain your answer. [2 marks]

Q2 On the right is a Maxwell-Boltzmann distribution curve for a sample of a substance at 25 °C.

a) Which of the curves X or Y shows the Maxwell-Boltzman distribution curve for the same sample at 15 °C ? [1 mark]

b) Explain how this curve shows that the reaction rate will be lower at 15 °C than at 25 °C. [2 marks]

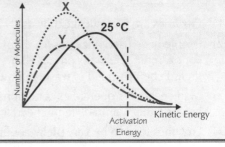

Reaction Rates — cheaper than water rates

*This page isn't too hard to learn — no equations, no formulas... what more could you ask for. The only tricky thing might be the Maxwell-Boltzmann thingymajiggle. Remember, increasing concentration and pressure do exactly the same thing. The only difference is you increase the concentration of a **solution** and the pressure of a **gas**. Don't get them muddled.*

Catalysts

Catalysts were tantalisingly mentioned on the last page — here's the full story...

Catalysts Increase the Rate of Reactions

You can use **catalysts** to make chemical reactions happen **faster**. Learn this definition:

> A **catalyst** increases the **rate** of a reaction by providing an **alternative reaction pathway** with a **lower activation energy**. The catalyst is **chemically unchanged** at the end of the reaction.

1) Catalysts are **great**. They **don't** get used up in reactions, so you only need a **tiny bit** of catalyst to catalyse a **huge** amount of stuff. They **do** take part in reactions, but they're **remade** at the end.

2) Catalysts are **very fussy** about which reactions they catalyse. Many will usually **only** work on a single reaction.

An example of a catalyst is **iron**. It's used in the **Haber process** to make ammonia.

$$N_{2(g)} + 3H_{2(g)} \xrightarrow{\text{Fe}_{(s)}} 2NH_{3(g)}$$

Enthalpy Profiles and Boltzmann Distributions Show Why Catalysts Work

If you look at an **enthalpy profile** together with a **Maxwell-Boltzmann Distribution**, you can see **why** catalysts work.

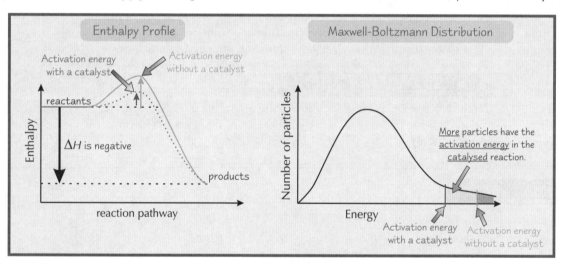

The catalyst **lowers the activation energy**, meaning there's **more particles** with **enough energy** to react when they collide. So, in a certain amount of time, **more particles react**.

Enzymes are Often Used in Industry Too

1) Enzymes are **biological catalysts** — they're **proteins** that catalyse certain **biochemical reactions**.

2) People have used enzymes for thousands of years — since way before we even knew what enzymes were. For example, enzymes produced by **yeast** are used to make bread and alcohol. More recent uses of enzymes include being added to **washing powders** to help break down stains and being used to partly digest **baby food**.

3) Many enzymes operate in conditions close to **room temperature and pressure**, so they're useful in **industry** because they can reduce the need for high temperature, fuel-guzzling processes.

4) Enzymes tend to be very **picky** about what they catalyse, and most can only be used for very **specific reactions**. This can be useful too — it means they can select one molecule from a mixture and cause that to react without affecting the others. This has been exploited in the production of new drugs.

Catalysts

Catalysts — Good for Industries...

Loads of industries rely on **catalysts**. They can dramatically lower production costs, and help make better products. Here's a few examples —

Iron is used as a catalyst in **ammonia** production. If it wasn't for the catalyst, they'd have to raise the **temperature** loads to make the reaction happen **quick enough**. Not only would this be bad for their fuel bills, it'd **reduce the amount of ammonia** produced.

Using a catalyst can change the properties of a product to make it more useful, e.g. **poly(ethene)**.

	Made without a catalyst	Made with a catalyst (a Ziegler-Natta catalyst to be precise)
Properties of poly(ethene)	less dense, less rigid	more dense, more rigid, higher melting point

Catalysts are used **loads** in the **petroleum industry** too.
They're used for **cracking**, **isomerisation**, and **reforming** alkanes (see p56-57).

...And for the Environment

1) Using catalysts means that lower temperatures and pressures can be used. So energy is saved, meaning **less CO$_2$** is released, and fossil fuel reserves are preserved. They can also **reduce waste** by allowing a different reaction to be used with a better **atom economy**. (See page 52 for more on atom economy.)

> For example, making the painkiller ibuprofen by the traditional method involves 6 steps and has an atom economy of 32%. Using catalysts it can be made in **3 steps** with an **atom economy of 77%**.

2) **Catalytic converters** on cars are made from **alloys of platinum, palladium and rhodium**. They reduce the pollution released into the atmosphere by speeding up the reaction $2CO + 2NO \rightarrow 2CO_2 + N_2$.

> But catalysts don't last forever. All catalysts eventually need to be disposed of. The trouble is, many contain nasty **toxic** compounds, which may leach into the soil if they're sent directly to **landfill**. So it's important to try to recycle them, or convert them to non-leaching forms.
>
> If catalysts contain **valuable metals**, such as platinum, it's worth recovering and recycling it — and there's special companies eager to do this. The decision whether to recycle the catalyst or to send it to landfill is made by balancing the **economic and environmental factors**.

Practice Questions

Q1 Explain what a catalyst is.

Q2 Draw an enthalpy profile diagram and a Maxwell-Boltzmann distribution diagram to show how a catalyst works.

Q3 Describe three reasons why catalysts are useful for industry.

Exam Questions

Q1 Sulfuric acid is manufactured by the contact process. In one of the stages, sulfur dioxide is converted into sulfur trioxide. A vanadium(V) oxide catalyst is used.

$$2SO_{2(g)} + O_{2(g)} \xrightarrow{\quad V_2O_{5(s)} \quad} 2SO_{3(g)} \qquad \Delta H = -197 \text{ kJ mol}^{-1}$$

   a) Draw and label an enthalpy profile diagram for the catalysed reaction. Label the activation energy.   [3 marks]

   b) On your diagram from part a), sketch a profile for the uncatalysed reaction.   [1 mark]

   c) Explain how catalysts work.   [2 marks]

Q2 The decomposition of hydrogen peroxide, H_2O_2, into water and oxygen is catalysed by manganese(IV) oxide, MnO_2.

   a) Write an equation for the reaction.   [2 marks]

   b) Sketch a Maxwell-Boltzmann distribution for the reaction.
     Mark on the activation energy for the catalysed and uncatalysed process.   [3 marks]

   c) Referring to your diagram from part b), explain how manganese(IV) oxide acts as a catalyst.   [3 marks]

I'm a catalyst — I like to speed up arguments without getting too involved...

Whatever you do, do not confuse the Maxwell-Boltzmann diagram for catalysts with the one for a temperature change. Catalysts lower the activation energy without changing the shape of the curve. BUT, the shape of the curve does change with temperature. Get these mixed up and you'll be the laughing stock of the Examiners' tea room.

Dynamic Equilibrium

There's a lot of to-ing and fro-ing on this page. Mind your head doesn't start spinning.

Reversible Reactions Can Reach Dynamic Equilibrium

1) Lots of chemical reactions are **reversible** — they go **both ways**. To show a reaction's reversible, you stick in a $\rightleftharpoons$. Here's an example:

$$H_{2(g)} + I_{2(g)} \rightleftharpoons 2HI_{(g)}$$

This reaction can go in **either direction** —

forwards $H_{2(g)} + I_{2(g)} \rightarrow 2HI_{(g)}$ ...or backwards $2HI_{(g)} \rightarrow H_{2(g)} + I_{2(g)}$

2) As the **reactants** get used up, the **forward** reaction **slows down** — and as more **product** is formed, the **reverse** reaction **speeds up**.

3) After a while, the forward reaction will be going at exactly the **same rate** as the backward reaction. The amounts of reactants and products **won't be changing** any more, so it'll seem like **nothing's happening**. It's a bit like you're **digging a hole**, while someone else is **filling it in** at exactly the **same speed**. This is called a **dynamic equilibrium**.

4) A **dynamic equilibrium** can only happen in a **closed system**. This just means nothing can get in or out.

Le Chatelier's Principle Predicts what will Happen if Conditions are Changed

If you **change** the **concentration**, **pressure** or **temperature** of a reversible reaction, you tend to **alter** the **position of equilibrium**. This just means you'll end up with **different amounts** of reactants and products at equilibrium.

If the position of equilibrium moves to the **left**, you'll get more **reactants**.

$$H_{2(g)} + I_{2(g)} \rightleftharpoons 2HI_{(g)}$$

If the position of equilibrium moves to the **right**, you'll get more **products**.

$$H_{2(g)} + I_{2(g)} \rightleftharpoons 2HI_{(g)}$$

Le Chatelier's principle tells you how the **position of equilibrium** will change if a **condition changes**:

If there's a change in **concentration**, **pressure** or **temperature**, the equilibrium will move to help **counteract** the change.

So, basically, if you **raise the temperature**, the position of equilibrium will shift to try to **cool things down**. And, if you **raise the pressure or concentration**, the position of equilibrium will shift to try to **reduce it again**.

Here Are Some Handy Rules for Using Le Chatelier's Principle

CONCENTRATION . $2SO_{2(g)} + O_{2(g)} \rightleftharpoons 2SO_{3(g)}$

1) If you **increase** the **concentration** of a **reactant** (SO_2 or O_2), the equilibrium tries to **get rid of** the extra reactant. It does this by making **more product** (SO_3). So the equilibrium's shifted to the **right**.

2) If you **increase** the **concentration** of the **product** (SO_3), the equilibrium tries to remove the extra product. This makes the **reverse reaction** go faster. So the equilibrium shifts to the **left**.

3) **Decreasing** the concentrations has the **opposite effect**.

PRESSURE

(changing this only affects **equilibria involving gases**)

1) **Increasing** the pressure shifts the equilibrium to the side with **fewer** gas molecules. This **reduces** the pressure.

2) **Decreasing** the pressure shifts the equilibrium to the side with **more** gas molecules. This **raises** the pressure again.

There are 3 moles on the left, but only 2 on the right. So, an increase in pressure shifts the equilibrium to the right.

$$2SO_{2(g)} + O_{2(g)} \rightleftharpoons 2SO_{3(g)}$$

TEMPERATURE

1) If you **increase** the temperature, you **add heat**. The equilibrium shifts in the **endothermic** (positive ΔH) direction to absorb this heat.

2) **Decreasing** the temperature **removes heat**. The equilibrium shifts in the **exothermic** (negative ΔH) direction to try to replace the heat.

3) If the forward reaction's **endothermic**, the reverse reaction will be **exothermic**, and vice versa.

This reaction's exothermic in the forward direction. If you increase the temperature, the equilibrium shifts to the left to absorb the extra heat.

Exothermic $\Longrightarrow$

$$2SO_{2(g)} + O_{2(g)} \rightleftharpoons 2SO_{3(g)} \quad \Delta H = -197 \text{ kJ mol}^{-1}$$

$\Longleftarrow$ Endothermic

Dynamic Equilibrium

Catalysts *Don't Affect* The Position of Equilibrium

Catalysts have **NO EFFECT** on the **position of equilibrium**.
They **can't** increase **yield** — but they **do** mean equilibrium is reached **faster**.

Ethanol can be formed from *Ethene* and *Steam*

1) The industrial production of **ethanol** is a good example of why Le Chatelier's principle is important in **real life**.

2) Ethanol is produced via a **reversible exothermic reaction** between ethene and **steam**:

$$C_2H_{4(g)} + H_2O_{(g)} \rightleftharpoons C_2H_5OH_{(g)} \qquad \Delta H = \text{-46 kJ mol}^{-1}$$

3) The reaction is carried out at a pressure of **60-70 atmospheres** and a temperature of **300 °C**, with a **phosphoric(V) acid** catalyst.

The *Conditions* Chosen are a *Compromise*

1) Because it's an **exothermic reaction**, **lower** temperatures favour the forward reaction. This means **more** ethane and steam is converted to ethanol at lower temperatures — you get a better **yield**.

2) But **lower temperatures** mean a **slower rate of reaction**. You'd be **daft** to try to get a **really high yield** of ethanol if it's going to take you 10 years. So the 300 °C is a **compromise** between **maximum yield** and **a faster reaction**.

3) **Higher pressures** favour the **forward reaction,** so a pressure of **60-70 atmospheres** is used — **high pressure** moves the reaction to the side with **fewer molecules of gas**. **Increasing the pressure** also increases the **rate** of reaction.

4) Cranking up the pressure as high as you can sounds like a great idea so far. But **high pressures** are **expensive** to produce. You need **stronger pipes** and **containers** to withstand high pressure. In this process, increasing the pressure can also cause **side reactions** to occur.

5) So the **60-70 atmospheres** is a **compromise** between **maximum yield** and **expense**. In the end, it all comes down to **minimising costs**.

Mr and Mrs Le Chatelier celebrate another successful year in the principle business

Practice Questions

Q1 Using an example, explain the terms 'reversible' and 'dynamic equilibrium'.

Q2 If the equilibrium moves to the right, do you get more products or reactants?

Q3 A reaction at equilibrium is endothermic in the forward direction. What happens to the position of equilibrium as the temperature is increased?

Exam Question

Q1 Nitrogen and oxygen gases were reacted together in a closed flask and allowed to reach equilibrium with the nitrogen monoxide formed. The forward reaction is endothermic.

$$N_{2(g)} + O_{2(g)} \rightleftharpoons 2NO_{(g)}$$

a) State Le Chatelier's principle. [1 mark]

b) Explain how the following changes would affect the position of equilibrium of the above reaction:
   (i) Pressure is **increased**. [2 marks]
   (ii) Temperature is **reduced**. [2 marks]
   (iii) Nitrogen monoxide is removed. [1 mark]

c) What would be the effect of a catalyst on the composition of the equilibrium mixture? [1 mark]

Only going forward cos we can't find reverse...

Equilibria never do what you want them to do. They always **oppose** *you. Be sure you know what happens to an equilibrium if you change the conditions. A word about pressure — if there's the same number of gas moles on each side of the equation, then you can raise the pressure as high as you like and it won't make a blind bit of difference to the position of equilibrium.*

Green Chemistry

'Green' things are big news these days — they're everywhere. So it'll be no surprise to find them in AS Chemistry too.

Chemical Industries Could Be More Sustainable

1) Doing something **sustainably** means doing it **without stuffing things up** for the future. Sustainable chemistry (or 'green chemistry') means you don't **use up** all the Earth's **resources**, or put loads of **damaging** chemicals into the environment.

2) Many of the chemical processes used in industry at the moment **aren't** very sustainable. Take the **plastics** industry, for example — the raw materials used often come from non-renewable **crude oil**, and the products themselves are usually **non-biodegradable** or **hard to recycle** when we're finished with them. (See pages 64-65 for more details.)

3) But there are things chemists can do to try and improve things. For example, they can...

USE RENEWABLE RAW MATERIALS

Loads of chemicals are traditionally made from **non-renewable** raw materials (e.g. crude oil fractions, or metal ores). But chemists can often develop **alternative compounds** (or **alternative ways** to make existing ones) involving **renewable** raw materials — e.g. some plastics are now made from **plant products** rather than oil fractions (p65).

USE RENEWABLE ENERGY SOURCES

Many chemical processes use a lot of **energy**. Right now, most of that energy comes from **fossil fuels**, which will soon run out. But there are potential **alternatives**...

- **Plant-based fuels** can be used (e.g. bioethanol — see page 59 for more).
- **Solar power** — ways to produce electricity from sunlight are developing rapidly.

There are other renewable energy technologies — like geothermal, wind, wave...

ENSURE ALL THE CHEMICALS INVOLVED ARE AS NON-TOXIC AS POSSIBLE

1) Many common chemicals are **harmful** — either to **humans**, other **living things**, the **environment**, or all three. Where possible, it's generally a good thing to use a **safer** alternative. For example...

- **Lead** (which can have some nasty effects on your health) used to be used in paint, petrol and for soldering. Alternatives are now used — paint and petrol use lead-free compounds, solder can be made with other metals.
- Some **foams** used in fire extinguishers are very good at putting out fires, but leave hazardous products behind, including some that deplete the ozone layer (see page 94). Again, alternatives are now available.
- **Dry cleaners** used to use a solvent based on chlorinated **hydrocarbons**, but these are known to be **carcinogenic** (i.e. they cause cancer). Safer alternatives are now available (liquid 'supercritical' carbon dioxide, as you asked).

2) Sometimes **redesigning** a **process** means you can do without unsafe chemicals completely — e.g. instead of using harmful organic solvents, some reactions can be carried out with one of the **reactants** acting as a solvent.

MAKE SURE THAT PRODUCTS AND WASTE ARE BIODEGRADABLE OR RECYCLABLE

1) Chemists can try to create **recyclable** products (see p64) — a good way to conserve raw materials.

2) **Waste** should be kept to a **minimum**, and preferably be **recyclable** or **biodegradable** (see p65).

3) You can also improve **sustainability** by developing more **efficient processes** — for example, by using **catalysts** (see p86-87), or by picking reactions with higher **atom economy** (see p52).

4) **Laws** can be used to encourage change. For example, when you buy a new TV, the shop now has to agree to recycle your old TV set, with the TV manufacturers paying some of the cost. This creates an incentive to design products that are easier and cheaper to recycle.

Plastics are hard to recycle. Dogs too.

Greener Chemistry Can Have Unexpected Consequences

Pretty much everyone agrees that making the chemical industry more sustainable is a good thing. But sometimes making things 'greener' can cause unwanted **knock-on effects**. Take biofuels, for example...

- Growing grain for biodiesel (or sugar cane for ethanol) means **less land** is available to grow **food**. So food gets **more expensive** — which will be worst for the **urban poor**, who already struggle to afford food (and can't grow their own).
- Large biofuel companies might buy up the **most fertile** land, forcing small farmers onto land with poorer crop yields.
- The land to grow biofuels often comes from clearing **forests**. Removing loads of trees means less CO_2 is absorbed in photosynthesis, so more stays in the atmosphere — the very problem that the use of biofuels is supposed to tackle...
- And that's not all — destroying existing, varied habitats and replacing them all with vast swathes of the same crop will **reduce biodiversity** and could cause **soil degradation** (loss of nutrients, etc.).

Green Chemistry

International Cooperation Is Needed to Reduce Pollution

1) Pollution doesn't stop at national borders — **rivers** flow from one country to the next, and the **atmosphere** and **oceans** are constantly moving and mixing. This means that eventually **everyone** suffers from **everyone else's** dirty ways.

2) **International cooperation** is important — there are already concerns about countries buying products made using **polluting technologies** from **abroad**, so that they can claim not to be producing the pollution themselves.

3) Various **international treaties** have been agreed. But usually, not all countries sign up because they're worried it will be bad for their **economy** (make things more expensive, cause job losses, and so on).

4) The **Montreal Protocol on Substances that Deplete the Ozone Layer** is probably the most successful 'green chemistry' global treaty to date — virtually everyone's signed up. Countries who signed up to this '**Montreal Protocol**' agreed to phase out production of substances that damaged the ozone layer (see p94).

5) Similarly, most countries have signed the **Stockholm Treaty** on persistent organic pollutants (POPs). POPs are organic chemicals (e.g. some pesticides and fungicides) that **accumulate** in the fatty tissues of living organisms. They're passed up the food chain and are **toxic** to humans and other animals.

6) In 1992, the United Nations held a big conference about the environment and development (the '**Earth Summit**') in Rio de Janeiro. Governments agreed to a set of **27 principles** about sustainable development — the 'Rio Declaration'.

These principles were all very sensible (e.g. don't cause environmental harm, develop in a sustainable way, and so on) but they **aren't legally binding** — so **no punishment** can be dished out when countries don't keep to the principles.

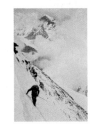

The summit of the Earth... much harder to get to than the Earth Summit in Rio had been.

You *don't* need to memorise *every detail* about the examples on these last two pages, but you should understand the *basic principles* behind them.

Practice Questions

Q1 List four ways in which the chemical industry can be made more sustainable.

Q2 Give two examples of renewable energy sources.

Q3 List four potential drawbacks of biofuel production.

Q4 Why are international treaties important in controlling pollution?

Exam Questions

Q1 In Brazil, ethanol is produced by fermenting sugar cane. This ethanol is then used as fuel.

a) Explain the advantages of using ethanol made from sugar cane as a fuel, instead of petrol. [2 marks]

b) Suggest why not all countries produce ethanol for use as a fuel in this way. [1 mark]

c) Describe two possible negative effects of growing sugar cane to make ethanol. [2 marks]

Q2 Much research is currently done on new catalysts.

a) Explain why catalysts are important in making chemical processes 'greener'. [2 marks]

b) The discovery of a new catalyst has made it possible to make ethanoic acid very efficiently by reacting methanol with carbon monoxide:

$$CH_3OH + CO \rightarrow CH_3COOH$$

Describe one way in which this process could be considered 'green'. [2 marks]

Like the contents of my fridge, Chemistry's going greener by the day...

It's important stuff, all this. It'll be important for your exam, obviously, but it's my bet that you'll come across this stuff long after you've taken your exam as well, which makes it doubly useful. On a different note... isn't it weird how you can sign up for an AS level in Chemistry, and only then be told that you'll be studying international politics too...

The Greenhouse Effect

Now I'm sure you know this already but it's good to be sure — the greenhouse effect, global warming and climate change are all different things. They're linked (and you need to know how) — but they are not the same. Ahem.

The **Greenhouse Effect** *Keeps Us* **Alive**

1) Some of the **electromagnetic radiation** from the Sun reaches the Earth and is **absorbed**. The Earth then **re-emits** it as **infrared radiation** (heat).

2) Various gases in the troposphere (the lowest layer of the atmosphere) **absorb** some of this infrared radiation... and **re-emit** it in **all directions** — including back towards Earth, keeping us warm. This is called the '**greenhouse effect**' (even though a real greenhouse doesn't actually work like this, annoyingly).

3) The main greenhouse gases are **water vapour**, **carbon dioxide** and **methane**. Their molecules **absorb IR radiation** to make the bonds in the molecule **vibrate more**. This extra energy is passed on to other molecules in the air by **collisions**, giving the other molecules more kinetic energy and raising the overall temperature.

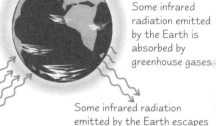

Visible and UV radiation from the Sun

Some infrared radiation emitted by the Earth is absorbed by greenhouse gases

Some infrared radiation emitted by the Earth escapes

4) The contribution of any particular gas to the greenhouse effect depends on:

   • how much radiation one molecule of the gas absorbs

   • how much of that gas there is in the atmosphere (concentration in ppm, say)

For example, one methane molecule traps far more heat than one carbon dioxide molecule, but there's much **less methane** in the atmosphere, so its overall contribution to the greenhouse effect is smaller.

An **Enhanced Greenhouse Effect** *Causes* **Global Warming**

1) Over the last 150 years or so, the world's **human population** has shot up and we've become more **industrialised**. We've been **burning fossil fuels**, releasing **tons** of CO_2, and we've been **chopping down forests** which used to absorb CO_2 by photosynthesis.

2) **Methane** levels have risen as we've grown more food. **Cows** produce large amounts of methane (from both ends). Paddy fields, in which rice is grown, kick out a fair bit of it too.

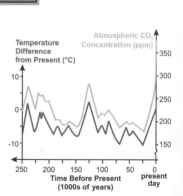

3) These **human activities** have caused a rise in greenhouse gas concentrations, which **enhances** the greenhouse effect. **More heat** is being trapped and the Earth is **getting warmer** — this is **global warming**.

> Global warming won't just make everywhere a bit warmer and affect the skiing — the warmer oceans will expand and massive ice-sheets in the polar regions will melt, causing **sea levels** to rise and leading to more flooding.
>
> The **climate** in any region of the world depends on a **really complicated** system of ocean currents, winds, etc. Global warming means there's **more heat energy** in the system. This could lead to **stormier**, less predictable weather.
>
> In some places there could be much **less rainfall**, with droughts and crop failures causing famines and forcing entire populations to become refugees.
> In other regions, increased rainfall and flooding would bring diseases like cholera.

There's **Scientific Evidence** *for the Increase in Global Warming*

1) Scientists have collected data to confirm whether or not climate change is happening, e.g. from analysing air samples and sea water samples.

2) The evidence suggests that the Earth's average temperature has increased **dramatically** in the last 50 years, and that CO_2 levels have increased at the same time.

3) The **correlation** between CO_2 and temperature is pretty clear, but there's been debate about whether rising carbon dioxide levels have **caused** the recent temperature rise, and if so, what's caused the rising CO_2 levels. Just showing a correlation doesn't prove that one thing causes another — there has to be a plausible mechanism for how one change causes the other (in this case, the explanation is the enhanced greenhouse effect).

4) Most climate scientists now agree that the link **is** causal, and that recent warming is **anthropogenic** — **human activities** are to blame for the rise in CO_2 levels.

Temperature Difference from Present (°C)

Atmospheric CO_2 Concentration (ppm)

Time Before Present (1000s of years)

present day

The Greenhouse Effect

Scientists are **Monitoring Global Warming**...

1) Scientific evidence gathered by the Intergovernmental Panel on Climate Change (IPCC) persuaded most of the world's governments that global warming is happening. There's now **global agreement** that climate change could be very damaging for millions of people, the environment and economies, and that we should try to **limit** it.

2) In 1997 the **Kyoto protocol** was signed — industrialised countries (including the UK) promised to reduce their greenhouse gas emissions to agreed levels. Many chemists are now involved in **monitoring** greenhouse gas emissions to see if countries will meet the targets (it looks like many won't).

3) Chemists also continue to monitor the environment to see how it's changing now. The data they collect and analyse is used in **climate models** (a big load of equations run on a computer to simulate how the climate system works).

HANK MORGAN / SCIENCE PHOTO LIBRARY

4) Climate scientists use these models to predict future changes. It's a big job — when **new factors** affecting the climate are discovered by other scientists, the modellers have to 'tweak' their models to take this into account.

...and **Investigating** Ways to **Limit It**

Scientists are investigating various ways to help **reduce** carbon dioxide emissions. These include:

1) **Carbon capture and storage** (CCS). This means removing waste CO_2 from, say, power stations, and either
   - injecting it as a **liquid** into the **deep ocean**, or
   - storing it deep **underground** — one possibility is to use old oil- or gas-fields under the sea-bed, or
   - reacting it with metal oxides to form stable, easily stored **carbonate minerals**, e.g. calcium carbonate.

2) Developing alternative fuels. See pages 58-59 for more on this.

Practice Questions

Q1 What type of electromagnetic radiation does the Earth emit?

Q2 What's the difference between the greenhouse effect and global warming?

Q3 Give three reasons why climate change is seen as a problem.

Exam Questions

Q1 a) Name the three main greenhouse gases. [3 marks]

b) Explain how greenhouse gases keep the temperature in the lower layer of the Earth's atmosphere higher than it would otherwise be. [3 marks]

c) What factors affect the contribution a gas makes to the greenhouse effect? [2 marks]

Q2 The concentration of carbon dioxide in the Earth's atmosphere has increased over the last 50 years.

a) Give two reasons for this increase. [2 marks]

b) How do governments know that global warming is happening? [1 mark]

c) Describe two methods that chemists are developing as a way of reducing carbon dioxide emissions. [2 marks]

Global Warming probably just isn't funny...

You may be sick of global warming, because it's all over the news these days. But how scientists gathered all the evidence to back up the theory that global warming is caused by human activity is a great example of How Science Works. What's more, the evidence was used to instigate an international treaty — a beauty of an example of how science informs decision-making.

The Ozone Layer and Air Pollution

Three pages on air pollution coming up, so take a deep breath...
unless you're hanging around somewhere with a lot of air pollution, that is...

The Earth has a Layer of Ozone at the Edge of the Stratosphere

The **ozone layer** is in a layer of the atmosphere called the **stratosphere**. It contains most of the atmosphere's **ozone molecules**, O_3. Ozone is formed when **UV radiation** from the Sun hits oxygen molecules.

> If the right amount of **UV radiation** is absorbed by an oxygen molecule, the oxygen molecule splits into separate atoms or **free radicals**. The free radicals then **combine** with other oxygen molecules to form **ozone molecules**, O_3.
>
> $$O_2 + h\nu \rightarrow O\bullet + O\bullet \longrightarrow O_2 + O\bullet \rightarrow O_3$$
>
> *a quantum of UV radiation*

The Ozone Layer is Constantly Being Replaced

1) UV radiation can also **reverse** the formation of ozone.

$$O_3 + h\nu \rightarrow O_2 + O\bullet$$

The radical produced then forms more ozone with an O_2 molecule, as shown above.

2) So, the ozone layer is continuously being **destroyed** and **replaced** as UV radiation hits the molecules. An **equilibrium** is set up, so the concentrations stay fairly constant:

$$O_2 + O\bullet \rightleftharpoons O_3$$

The Ozone Layer Protects the Earth

1) The **UV radiation** from the Sun is made up of **different frequencies**. These are grouped into **three bands**:

UVA   UVB   UVC
→ INCREASING FREQUENCY AND ENERGY

2) The ozone layer removes all the high energy **UVC radiation** and about 90% of the **UVB**. These types of UV radiation are harmful to humans and most other life on Earth.

3) **UVB** can damage the DNA in cells and cause **skin cancer**. It's the main cause of **sunburn** too. **UVA** can also lead to **skin cancer**. Both types of UV break down collagen fibres in the skin causing it to **age faster**.

4) When the skin's exposed to UV, it **tans**. This helps protect **deeper tissues** from the effects of the radiation.

5) **BUT...** UV radiation isn't all bad — in fact it's **essential** for us humans. We need it to produce **vitamin D**.

CFCs and Nitrogen Oxides Break Ozone Down

1) In the 1970s and 1980s, scientists discovered that the **ozone layer** above **Antarctica** was getting **thinner** — in fact, it was decreasing very rapidly. The ozone layer over the **Arctic** has been found to be thinning too. These 'holes' in the ozone layer are bad because they allow more harmful **UVB radiation** to reach the Earth.

2) **CFCs** (see p72) absorb UV radiation and split to form **chlorine free radicals**. These free radicals **destroy ozone molecules** and are then **regenerated** to destroy more ozone. One chlorine atom can destroy 10 000 ozone molecules before it forms a stable compound.

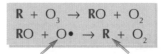

Here's a satellite map showing the 'hole' in the ozone layer over Antarctica. The 'hole' is shown by the white and pink area.

LABORATORY FOR ATMOSPHERES, NASA GODDARD SPACE FLIGHT CENTER/SCIENCE PHOTO LIBRARY

3) **NO•** free radicals from **nitrogen oxides** destroy ozone too. Nitrogen oxides are produced by **car and aircraft engines** and **thunderstorms**. NO• free radicals affect ozone in the **same way** as chlorine radicals.

4) The reactions can be represented by these equations, where **R** represents either Cl• or NO•.

$$R + O_3 \rightarrow RO + O_2$$
$$RO + O\bullet \rightarrow R + O_2$$

NO• and Cl• aren't the only culprits — free radicals are produced from other halogenoalkanes too.

The free radicals acts as **catalysts** for the destruction of the ozone.

Formed when UV breaks down O_2.   *The harmful radical is regenerated.*

The overall reaction is: $$O_3 + O\bullet \rightarrow 2O_2$$

The Ozone Layer and Air Pollution

CFCs and nitrogen oxides breaking the ozone layer down isn't the only air pollution problem you need to know about...

Burning **Hydrocarbons** can Produce **Carbon Monoxide**

Fuels from crude oil are used all the time, for things such as transport and in power stations.

1) When pure alkanes burn **completely**, all you get is **carbon dioxide** and **water**.

2) But if there's **not enough oxygen**, hydrocarbons combust **incompletely**, and you get **carbon monoxide** gas produced instead of carbon dioxide. This can happen in internal combustion engines (as used in most cars on the planet).

> Here's how carbon monoxide forms when methane burns without enough oxygen:
> $$CH_{4\,(g)} + 1\frac{1}{2}O_{2\,(g)} \rightarrow CO_{(g)} + 2H_2O_{(g)}$$
> And here's the equation for incomplete combustion of octane:
> $$C_8H_{18\,(g)} + 8\frac{1}{2}O_{2\,(g)} \rightarrow 8CO_{(g)} + 9H_2O_{(g)}$$

3) This is bad news — carbon monoxide gas is poisonous. Carbon monoxide molecules bind to the same sites on **haemoglobin molecules** in red blood cells as oxygen molecules. So **oxygen** can't be carried around the body.

And if that's Not Bad Enough... **Burning Fuels** Produces Other **Pollutants** Too

Carbon monoxide's not the only pollutant gas that comes out of a car exhaust.

1) Engines **don't burn** all the fuel molecules. Some of these come out as **unburnt hydrocarbons**.

2) **Oxides of nitrogen** (NO_x) are produced when the high pressure and temperature in a car engine cause the nitrogen and oxygen atoms in the air to react together. Oxides of nitrogen don't just contribute to the breaking down of the ozone layer...

3) The hydrocarbons and nitrogen oxides react with sunlight to form **ground-level ozone** (O_3), which is a major component of **smog**. Specifically, it's part of **photochemical smog** — the dangerous chemicals that form when certain pollutant gases react with sunlight.

4) **Ground-level ozone** irritates people's eyes, aggravates respiratory problems and even damages our lungs (ozone isn't very nice stuff, unless it is high up in the atmosphere as part of the ozone layer).

Luckily, carbon monoxide, unburnt hydrocarbons and oxides of nitrogen can be removed by **catalytic converters** on cars. Unluckily, you need to know some of the chemistry behind them...

Catalytic Converters Reduce Harmful Exhaust Emissions

1) Catalytic converters sit quietly in a car **exhaust** and get rid of **pollutant gases** like carbon monoxide, oxides of nitrogen and unburnt hydrocarbons by changing them to **harmless gases**, like water vapour and nitrogen, or to **less harmful** ones like carbon dioxide.

a cat   a list

2) **Solid** heterogeneous catalysts can provide a **surface** for a reaction to take place on. Here's how it works —

- **Reactant molecules** arrive at the **surface** and **bond** with the solid catalyst. This is called **a<u>d</u>sorption**.

- The bonds between the **reactant's** atoms are **weakened** and **break up**. This forms **radicals**. These radicals then **get together** and make **new molecules**.

- The new molecules are then detached from the catalyst. This is called **desorption**.

> This example shows you how a catalytic converter changes the harmful gases **nitrogen monoxide, NO**, and **carbon monoxide, CO**, to **nitrogen** and **carbon dioxide**.
>
> (O)(N) (N)(O) (C)(O)   Adsorption of NO and CO to the catalyst.
> ――――――――――
> Catalyst surface
>
> Chemical reaction — PIZZAZZ — N_2 and CO_2 are formed.
>
> (O)(N) (N)(O) (C)(O)   Desorption of N_2 and CO_2 from the catalyst.
> ――――――――――
> Catalyst surface

Remember — the adsorption **mustn't** be **too strong** or it won't **let go** of the atoms. **BUT** — it needs to be **strong enough** to **weaken** the bonds between the reactant molecules so that the new molecules can form.

The Ozone Layer and Air Pollution

Infrared Spectroscopy is Used to Monitor Air Pollution

You can use **infrared spectroscopy** to measure how much of a **polluting gas** is present in the **air**.
(If you've forgotten what infrared spectroscopy is, go back and look at page 75.)

Here's an outline of how infrared spectroscopy is used to check how much **carbon monoxide** there is:

1) A **sample of air** is drawn into the spectrometer. A beam of **infrared radiation** of a certain frequency is passed through the sample. Any carbon monoxide that is present will **absorb** some of this radiation.

2) At the same time, a beam of infrared radiation of the **same frequency** is passed through a sample of a gas that **doesn't absorb any infrared**, like N_2. This acts as a kind of **control** reading.

3) The **difference** in the amount of infrared energy absorbed by the gases in the two chambers is a measure of the **amount** of carbon monoxide present in the air sample.

You can use the same technique to monitor the levels of any polluting gas that can absorb infrared, like NO, SO_2 or CH_4. Only molecules containing at least two different atoms will absorb infrared radiation.

Practice Questions

Q1 What is ozone, and where is the ozone layer?

Q2 Which has higher energy — UVA, UVB, or UVC?

Q3 Write out equations to show how ozone is destroyed, using R to represent the radical.

Q4 Write a chemical equation for the incomplete combustion of methane gas in air.

Q5 What exhaust gases contribute to photochemical smog?

Q6 Describe how the catalytic converter in a car exhaust works.

Exam Questions

Q1 The 'ozone layer' lies mostly between 15 and 30 km above the Earth's surface.

a) Explain how ozone forms in this part of the atmosphere. [3 marks]

b) What are the benefits to humans of the ozone layer? [2 marks]

c) How does the ozone layer absorb harmful radiation without being permanently destroyed? [3 marks]

Q2 Nitrogen monoxide gas is a pollutant formed when internal combustion engines burn fuels.

a) Write a balanced chemical equation for the formation of nitrogen monoxide from oxygen and nitrogen gas. [2 marks]

b) Nitrogen monoxide is converted into NO_2 by reaction with oxygen. Write a balanced equation for this reaction. [2 marks]

c) Name an environmental problem resulting from NO_2 gas being released into the atmosphere. [1 mark]

If a stranger offers you nitrogen monoxide, just say NO, kids...

That's right, it's yet more pages about all the things we're doing to screw up the environment. Lucky all those chemists are there to invent catalytic converters and stuff to save us from ourselves. I think the best plan is to get rid of all cars and walk everywhere. Except when I've got a lot of stuff to carry. Or when I'm in a hurry. Or when I'm feeling a bit lazy. Or...

Practical and Investigative Skills

You're going to have to do some practical work too — and once you've done it, you have to make sense of your results...

Make it a **Fair Test** — Control your **Variables**

You probably know this all off by heart but it's easy to get mixed up sometimes. So here's a quick recap:

> **Variable** — A variable is a **quantity** that has the **potential to change**, e.g. mass. There are two types of variable commonly referred to in experiments:
> * **Independent variable** — the thing that you **change** in an experiment.
> * **Dependent variable** — the thing that you **measure** in an experiment.

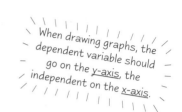

When drawing graphs, the dependent variable should go on the y-axis, the independent on the x-axis.

So, if you're investigating the effect of **temperature** on rate of reaction using the apparatus on the right, the variables will be:

Independent variable	Temperature
Dependent variable	Amount of oxygen produced — you can measure this by collecting it in a gas syringe
Other variables — you MUST keep these the same	Concentration and volume of solutions, mass of solids, pressure, the presence of a catalyst and the surface area of any solid reactants

Organise Your Results in a **Table** — And Watch Out For **Anomalous** Ones

Before you start your experiment, make a **table** to write your results in.
You'll need to repeat each test at least three times to check your results are reliable.

This is the sort of table you might end up with when you investigate the effect of **temperature** on **reaction rate**.
(You'd then have to do the same for **different temperatures**.)

Temperature	Time (s)	Volume of gas evolved (cm³) Run 1	Volume of gas evolved (cm³) Run 2	Volume of gas evolved (cm³) Run 3	Average volume of gas evolved (cm³)
	10	8	7	8	7.7
20 °C	20	17	19	20	18.7
	30	28	(20)	30	29

Find the average of each set of repeated values.

You need to add them all up and divide by how many there are.

E.g.: (8 + 7 + 8) ÷ 3 = 7.7 cm³

Watch out for **anomalous results**. These are ones that don't fit in with the other values and are likely to be wrong. They're likely to be due to random errors — here the syringe plunger may have got stuck.
Ignore anomalous results when you calculate the average.

Know Your Different Sorts of **Data**

Experiments always involve some sort of measurement to provide **data**.
There are different types of data —

> **Discrete** — you get discrete data by **counting**. E.g. the number of bubbles produced in a reaction would be discrete. You can't have 1.25 bubbles. That'd be daft. Shoe size is another good example of a discrete variable.

> **Continuous** — a continuous variable can have **any value** on a scale. For example, the volume of gas produced or the mass of products from a reaction. You can never measure the exact value of a continuous variable.

> **Categoric** — a categoric variable has values that can be sorted into **categories**. For example, the colours of solutions might be blue, red and green. Or types of material might be wood, steel, glass.

> **Ordered (ordinal)** — Ordered data is similar to categoric, but the categories can be **put in order**. For example, if you classify reactions as 'slow', 'fairly fast' and 'very fast' you'd have ordered data.

Practical and Investigative Skills

Graphs: *Line, Bar or Scatter* — Use the *Best Type*

You'll usually be expected to make a **graph** of your results. Not only are graphs **pretty**, they make your data **easier to understand** — so long as you choose the right type.

Line graphs are best when you have **two sets of continuous data**. For example:

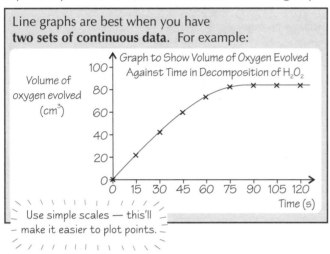

Graph to Show Volume of Oxygen Evolved Against Time in Decomposition of H_2O_2

Volume of oxygen evolved (cm^3)

Time (s)

Use simple scales — this'll make it easier to plot points.

You should use a bar chart when one of your data sets is **categoric or ordered data**. For example:

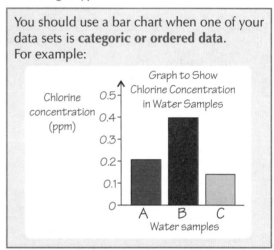

Chlorine concentration (ppm)

Graph to Show Chlorine Concentration in Water Samples

Water samples

Scatter plots are great for showing how two sets of data are related (or **correlated**).

Don't try to join all the points — draw a **line of best fit** to show the **trend**.

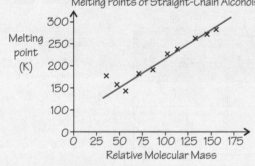

Scatter Graph to Show Relationship Between Relative Molecular Masses and Melting Points of Straight-Chain Alcohols

Melting point (K)

Relative Molecular Mass

Scatter Graphs Show The Relationship Between Variables

Correlation describes the **relationship** between two variables — the independent one and the dependent one.

Data can show:

1) **Positive correlation** — as one variable **increases** the other **increases**. The graph on the left shows positive correlation.

2) **Negative correlation** — as one variable **increases** the other **decreases**.

3) **No correlation** — there is **no relationship** between the two variables.

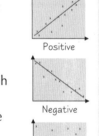

Positive

Negative

None

Whatever type of graph you make, you'll ONLY get full marks if you:

- Choose a sensible scale — don't do a tiny graph in the corner of the paper.
- Label both axes — including units.
- Plot your points accurately — using a sharp pencil.

There's also pie charts. These are normally used to display categoric data.

Correlation *Doesn't* Mean *Cause* — Don't Jump to Conclusions

1) Ideally, only **two** quantities would **ever** change in any experiment — everything else would remain **constant**.

2) But in experiments or studies outside the lab, you **can't** usually control all the variables. So even if two variables are correlated, the change in one may **not** be causing the change in the other. Both changes might be caused be a **third variable**.

Watch out for bias too — for instance, a bottled water company might point these studies out to people without mentioning any of the doubts.

| Example |

For example: Some studies have found a correlation between **drinking chlorinated tap water** and the risk of developing certain cancers. So some people argue that this means water shouldn't have chlorine added.

BUT it's hard to control all the variables between people who drink tap water and people who don't. It could be many lifestyle factors.

Or, the cancer risk could be affected by something else in tap water — or by whatever the non-tap water drinkers drink instead...

Practical and Investigative Skills

Don't Get **Carried Away** When Drawing Conclusions

The **data** should always **support** the conclusion. This may sound obvious but it's easy to **jump** to conclusions. Conclusions have to be **specific** — not make sweeping generalisations.

> **Example**
>
> The rate of an enzyme-controlled reaction was measured at **10 °C, 20 °C, 30 °C, 40 °C, 50 °C and 60 °C**. All other variables were kept constant, and the results are shown in this graph.
>
> A science magazine **concluded** from this data that enzyme X works best at **40 °C**. The data **doesn't** support this.
>
> The enzyme **could** work best at 42 °C or 47 °C but you can't tell from the data because **increases** of **10 °C** at a time were used. The rate of reaction at in-between temperatures **wasn't** measured.
>
> All you know is that it's faster at **40 °C** than at any of the other temperatures tested.

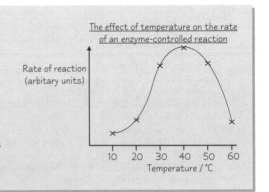

> **Example**
>
> The experiment above **ONLY** gives information about this particular enzyme-controlled reaction. You can't conclude that **all** enzyme-controlled reactions happen faster at a particular temperature — only this one. And you can't say for sure that doing the experiment at, say, a different constant pressure, wouldn't give a different optimum temperature.

You need to Look **Critically** at Your Results

There are a few bits of lingo that you need to understand. They'll be useful when you're evaluating how convincing your results are.

1) **Valid results** — Valid results answer the original question. For example, if you haven't **controlled all the variables** your results won't be valid, because you won't be testing just the thing you wanted to.

2) **Accurate** — Accurate results are those that are **really close** to the **true** answer.

3) **Precise results** — These are results taken using **sensitive instruments** that measure in **small increments**, e.g. pH measured with a meter (pH 7.692) will be **more precise** than pH measured with paper (pH 7).

   *It's possible for results to be precise **but not** accurate, e.g. a balance that weighs to 1/1000 th of a gram will give precise results but if it's not **calibrated** properly the results won't be accurate.*

   You may have to calculate the percentage error of a measurement.
   E.g. if a balance is calibrated to within 0.01 g, and you measure a mass as 4 g, then the percentage error is: (0.01 ÷ 4) × 100 = 0.25%.

4) **Reliable results** — **Reliable** means the results can be **consistently reproduced** in independent experiments. And if the results are reproducible they're more likely to be **true**. If the data isn't reliable for whatever reason you **can't draw** a valid **conclusion**.

   For experiments, the **more repeats** you do, the **more reliable** the data. If you get the **same result** twice, it could be the correct answer. But if you get the same result **20 times**, it'd be much more reliable. And it'd be even more reliable if everyone in the class got about the same results using different apparatus.

Work **Safely** and **Ethically** — Don't Blow Up the Lab or Harm Small Animals

In any experiment you'll be expected to show that you've thought about the **risks and hazards**. It's generally a good thing to wear an apron and goggles, but you may need to take additional safety measures, depending on the experiment. For example, anything involving nasty gases will need to be done in a fume cupboard.

You need to make sure you're working **ethically** too. This is most important if there are other people or animals involved. You have to put their welfare first.

Answers

Unit 1: Section 1 — Atoms and Reactions

Page 5 — The Atom

1) a) Similarity — They've all got the same number of protons/electrons. [1 mark]

   Difference — They all have different numbers of neutrons. [1 mark]

   b) 1 proton [1 mark], 1 neutron (2 − 1) [1 mark], 1 electron [1 mark].

   c) ^3H. [1 mark]

   Since tritium has 2 neutrons in the nucleus and also 1 proton, it has a mass number of 3. You could also write ^3_1H but you don't really need the atomic number.

2) a) (i) Same number of electrons. [1 mark]

   $^{32}S^{2-}$ has 16 + 2 = 18 electrons. ^{40}Ar has 18 electrons too. [1 mark]

   (ii) Same number of protons. [1 mark]

   Each has 16 protons (the atomic number of S must always be the same) [1 mark].

   (iii) Same number of neutrons. [1 mark]

   ^{40}Ar has 40 − 18 = 22 neutrons. ^{42}Ca has 42 − 20 = 22 neutrons. [1 mark]

   b) **A** and **C**. [1 mark] They have the same number of protons but different numbers of neutrons. [1 mark].

   It doesn't matter that they have a different number of electrons because they are still the same element.

Page 7 — Atomic Models

1) a) Bohr knew that if an electron was freely orbiting the nucleus it would spiral into it, causing the atom to collapse [1 mark]. His model only allowed electrons to be in fixed shells and not in between them [1 mark].

   b) When an electron moves from one shell to another electromagnetic radiation is emitted or absorbed [1 mark].

   c) Atoms react in order to gain full shells of electrons [1 mark]. Noble gases have full shells and so do not react [1 mark]. (Alternatively: a full shell of electrons makes an atom stable [1 mark]; noble gases have full shells and do not react because they are stable [1 mark].)

Page 9 — Relative Mass

1) a) First multiply each relative abundance by the relative mass —

   120.8 × 63 = 7610.4, 54.0 × 65 = 3510.0

   Next add up the products: 7610.4 + 3510.0 = 11 120.4 [1 mark]

   Now divide by the total abundance (120.8 + 54.0 = 174.8)

   $$A_r(Cu) = \frac{11\,120.4}{174.8} \approx \textbf{63.6}$$ [1 mark]

   You can check your answer by seeing if $A_r(Cu)$ is in between 63 and 65 (the lowest and highest relative isotopic masses).

   b) A sample of copper is a mixture of 2 isotopes in different abundances [1 mark]. The weighted average mass of these isotopes isn't a whole number [1 mark].

2) You use pretty much the same method here as for question 1)a).

   93.11 × 39 = 3631.29, 0.12 × 40 = 4.8, 6.77 × 41 = 277.57

   3631.29 + 4.8 + 277.57 = 3913.66 [1 mark]

   This time you divide by 100 because they're percentages.

   $$A_r(K) = \frac{3913.66}{100} \approx \textbf{39.14}$$ [1 mark]

   Again check your answer's between the lowest and highest relative isotopic masses, 39 and 41. $A_r(K)$ is closer to 39 because most of the sample (93.11 %) is made up of this isotope.

Page 11 — The Mole

1) M of CH_3COOH = (2 × 12) + (4 × 1) + (2 × 16) = 60 g mol^{-1} [1 mark]

   so mass of 0.36 moles = 60 × 0.36 = **21.6 g** [1 mark]

2) No. of moles = $\frac{0.25 \times 60}{1000}$ = 0.015 moles H_2SO_4 [1 mark]

   M of H_2SO_4 = (2 × 1) + (1 × 32) + (4 × 16) = 98 g mol^{-1}

   Mass of 0.015 H_2SO_4 = 98 x 0.015 = **1.47 g** [1 mark]

3) M of C_3H_8 = (3 × 12) + (8 × 1) = 44 g mol^{-1}

   No. of moles of C_3H_8 = $\frac{88}{44}$ = 2 moles [1 mark]

   At r.t.p. 1 mole of gas occupies 24 dm^3

   so 2 moles of gas occupies 2 x 24 = **48 dm^3** [1 mark]

Page 13 — Empirical and Molecular Formulas

1) Assume you've got 100 g of the compound so you can turn the % straight into mass.

   No. of moles of C = $\frac{92.3}{12}$ = 7.69 moles

   No. of moles of H = $\frac{7.7}{1}$ = 7.7 moles [1 mark]

   Divide both by the smallest number, in this case 7.69.

   So ratio C : H = 1 : 1

   So, the empirical formula = CH [1 mark]

   The empirical mass = 12 + 1 = 13

   No. of empirical units in molecule = $\frac{78}{13}$ = 6

   So the molecular formula = C_6H_6 [1 mark]

2) The magnesium is burning, so it's reacting with oxygen and the product is magnesium oxide.

   First work out the number of moles of each element.

   No. of moles Mg = $\frac{1.2}{24}$ = 0.05 moles

   Mass of O is everything that isn't Mg: 2 − 1.2 = 0.8 g

   No. of moles O = $\frac{0.8}{16}$ = 0.05 moles [1 mark]

   Ratio Mg : O = 0.05 : 0.05

   Divide both by the smallest number, in this case 0.05.

   So ratio Mg : O = 1 : 1

   So the empirical formula is MgO [1 mark]

3) First calculate the no. of moles of each product and then the mass of C and H:

   No. of moles of CO_2 = $\frac{33}{44}$ = 0.75 moles

   Mass of C = 0.75 × 12 = 9 g

   No. of moles of H_2O = $\frac{10.8}{18}$ = 0.6 moles

   0.6 moles H_2O = 1.2 moles H

   Mass of H = 1.2 × 1 = 1.2 g [1 mark]

   Organic acids contain C, H and O, so the rest of the mass must be O.

   Mass of O = 19.8 − (9 + 1.2) = 9.6 g

   No. of moles of O = $\frac{9.6}{16}$ = 0.6 moles [1 mark]

   Mole ratio = C : H : O = 0.75 : 1.2 : 0.6

   Divide by smallest   1.25 : 2 : 1

   This isn't a whole number ratio, so you have to multiply them all up until it is. Multiply them all by 4.

   So, mole ratio = C : H : O = 5 : 8 : 4

   Empirical formula = $C_5H_8O_4$ [1 mark]

   Empirical mass = (12 × 5) + (1 × 8) + (16 × 4) = 132 g

   This is the same as what we're told the molecular mass is, so the molecular formula is also $C_5H_8O_4$. [1 mark]

Page 15 — Equations and Calculations

1) M of C_2H_5Cl = (2 × 12) + (5 × 1) + (1 × 35.5) = 64.5 g mol^{-1} [1 mark]

   Number of moles of C_2H_5Cl = $\frac{258}{64.5}$ = 4 moles [1 mark]

   From the equation, 1 mole C_2H_5Cl is made from 1 mole C_2H_4 so, 4 moles C_2H_5Cl is made from 4 moles C_2H_4. [1 mark]

   M of C_2H_4 = (2 × 12) + (4 × 1) = 28 g mol^{-1}

   so, the mass of 4 moles C_2H_4 = 4 × 28 = **112 g** [1 mark]

2) a) M of $CaCO_3$ = 40 + 12 + (3 × 16) = 100 g mol^{-1}

   Number of moles of $CaCO_3$ = $\frac{15}{100}$ = 0.15 moles

   From the equation, 1 mole $CaCO_3$ produces 1 mole CaO so, 0.15 moles of $CaCO_3$ produces 0.15 moles of CaO. [1 mark]

   M of CaO = 40 + 16 = 56 g mol^{-1} [1 mark]

   so, mass of 0.15 moles of CaO = 56 × 0.15 = **8.4 g** [1 mark]

   b) From the equation, 1 mole $CaCO_3$ produces 1 mole CO_2 so, 0.15 moles of $CaCO_3$ produces 0.15 moles of CO_2. [1 mark]

   1 mole gas occupies 24 dm^3, [1 mark]

   so, 0.15 moles occupies = 24 × 0.15 = **3.6 dm^3** [1 mark]

3) On the LHS, you need 2 each of K and I, so use 2KI

   The final equation is: **2KI + Pb(NO$_3$)$_2$ → PbI$_2$ + 2KNO$_3$** [1 mark]

   In this equation, the NO_3 group remains unchanged, so it makes balancing much easier if you treat it as one indivisible lump.

Answers

Page 17 — Acids, Bases and Salts

1) a) $CaCO_{3(s)} + 2HClO_{4(aq)} \rightarrow Ca(ClO_4)_{2(aq)} + H_2O_{(l)} + CO_{2(g)}$

[1 mark for the state symbols, 1 mark for all the correct formulas and 1 mark for the correct balance.]

b) i) $2Li_{(s)} + 2H^+_{(aq)} \rightarrow 2Li^+_{(aq)} + H_{2(g)}$

[1 mark for the correct formulas, 1 mark for the correct balance.]
The SO_4^{2-} ions are left out of the ionic equation — they're spectator ions that don't get involved in the reaction.

ii) $2KOH_{(aq)} + H_2SO_{4(aq)} \rightarrow K_2SO_{4(aq)} + 2H_2O_{(l)}$

[1 mark for the correct formulas, 1 mark for the correct balance.]

iii) $2NH_{3(aq)} + H_2SO_{4(aq)} \rightarrow (NH_4)_2SO_{4(aq)}$

[1 mark for the correct formulas, 1 mark for the correct balance.]

2) a) M of $CaSO_4$ = 40 + 32 + (4 × 16) = 136 g mol^{-1} *[1 mark]*
no. moles = 1.133 g/136 = **0.00833 moles** *[1 mark]*

b) mass of water = difference in mass between hydrated and anhydrous salt = 1.883 − 1.133 = **0.750 g** *[1 mark]*

c) no. moles of water = mass/molar mass = 0.750/18 = 0.04167 *[1 mark]*
X = ratio of no. moles water to no. moles salt = 0.04167/0.00833 = 5.002 *[1 mark]*
Rounded to nearest integer **X = 5** *[1 mark]*

Page 19 — Titrations

1) First write down what you know:
CH_3COOH + $NaOH$ $\rightarrow$ CH_3COONa + H_2O
25.4 cm^3 14.6 cm^3
?   0.5 M

Number of moles of NaOH = $\dfrac{0.5 \times 14.6}{1000}$ = 0.0073 moles *[1 mark]*

From the equation, you know 1 mole of NaOH neutralises 1 mole of CH_3COOH, so if you've used 0.0073 moles NaOH you must have neutralised 0.0073 moles CH_3COOH. *[1 mark]*

Concentration of CH_3COOH = $\dfrac{0.0073 \times 1000}{25.4}$ = **0.287 M** *[1 mark]*

2) First write down what you know again:
$CaCO_3 + H_2SO_4 \rightarrow CaSO_4 + H_2O + CO_2$
0.75 g   0.25 M

M of $CaCO_3$ = 40 + 12 + (3 × 16) = 100 g mol^{-1} *[1 mark]*

Number of moles of $CaCO_3$ = $\dfrac{0.75}{100}$ = 7.5 × 10^{-3} moles *[1 mark]*

From the equation, 1 mole $CaCO_3$ reacts with 1 mole H_2SO_4 so, 7.5 × 10^{-3} moles $CaCO_3$ reacts with 7.5 × 10^{-3} moles H_2SO_4. *[1 mark]*

The volume needed is = $\dfrac{(7.5 \times 10^{-3}) \times 1000}{0.25}$ = 30 cm^3 *[1 mark]*

If the question mentions concentration or molarities, you can bet your last clean pair of underwear that you'll need to use the formula

number of moles = $\dfrac{\text{concentration} \times \text{volume}}{1000}$.

Just make sure the volume's in cm^3 though.

Page 21 — Oxidation and Reduction

1) a) H_2SO_4 (aq) + 8HI (aq) $\rightarrow H_2S$ (g) + 4I$_2$ (s) + 4H$_2$O (l) *[1 mark]*
b) Ox. No. of S in H_2SO_4 = +6 *[1 mark]*
Ox. No. of S in H_2S = −2 *[1 mark]*
c) Iodide *[1 mark]* — it donates electrons / its oxidation number increases *[1 mark]*

Unit 1: Section 2 — Electrons, Bonding and Structure

Page 23 — Electronic Structure

1) a) K atom: $1s^2 2s^2 2p^6 3s^2 3p^6 4s^1$ *[1 mark]*
K$^+$ ion: $1s^2 2s^2 2p^6 3s^2 3p^6$ *[1 mark]*
b) $1s^2 2s^2 2p^4$ *[1 mark]*
c) The outer shell electrons in potassium and oxygen can get close to the outer shells of other atoms, so they can be transferred or shared *[1 mark]*. The inner shell electrons are tightly held and shielded from the electrons in other atoms/molecules *[1 mark]*.

2) a) $1s^2 2s^2 2p^6 3s^2 3p^6 3d^5 4s^2$. *[1 mark]*
b) Germanium ($1s^2 2s^2 2p^6 3s^2 3p^6 3d^{10} 4s^2 4p^2$). *[1 mark]*. (The 4p sub-shell is partly filled, so it must be a p block element.)
c) Ar (atom) *[1 mark]*, K$^+$ (positive ion) *[1 mark]*, Cl$^-$ (negative ion) *[1 mark]*. You also could have suggested Ca^{2+}, S^{2-} or P^{3-}.
d) $1s^2 2s^2 2p^6$ *[1 mark]*

Page 25 — Ionisation Energies

1) a) Group 3 *[1 mark]*
There are three electrons removed before the first big jump in energy.
b) The electrons are being removed from an increasing positive charge *[1 mark]* so more energy is needed to remove an electron / the force of attraction that has to be broken is greater *[1 mark]*.
c) When an electron is removed from a different shell there is a big increase in the energy required (since that shell is closer to the nucleus) *[1 mark]*.
d) There are 3 shells (because there are 2 big jumps in energy) *[1 mark]*.

Page 27 — Ionic Bonding

1) a)

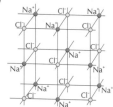

Your diagram should show the following —
• cubic structure with ions at corners *[1 mark]*
• sodium ions and chloride ions labelled *[1 mark]*
• alternating sodium ions and chloride ions *[1 mark]*
b) giant ionic/crystal (lattice) *[1 mark]*
c) You'd expect it to have a high melting point *[1 mark]*. Because there are strong bonds between the ions *[1 mark]* due to the electrostatic forces *[1 mark]*. A lot of energy is required to overcome these bonds *[1 mark]*.

2) a) Electrons move from one atom to another *[1 mark]*.
Any correct examples of ions, one positive, one negative.
E.g. Na$^+$, Cl$^-$. *[2 x 1 mark]*
b) In a solid, ions are held in place by strong ionic bonds *[1 mark]*. When the solid is heated to melting point, the ions gain enough energy *[1 mark]* to overcome the forces of attraction enough to become mobile *[1 mark]* and so carry charge (and hence electricity) through the substance *[1 mark]*.

Answers

Page 29 — Covalent Bonding

1) a) Covalent [1 mark]

   b)

   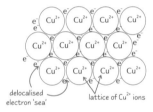

   Your diagram should show the following —
   • a completely correct electron arrangement [1 mark]
   • all 4 overlaps correct (one dot + one cross in each) [1 mark]

2 a) Dative covalent/coordinate bond [1 mark]

   b) One atom [1 mark] donates a pair of/both the electrons to the bond [1 mark].

Page 31 — Giant Molecular Structures & Metallic Bonding

1) a) Giant covalent lattice [1 mark]

   b) Diamond   Graphite   [1 mark for each correctly drawn diagram]

   Diamond's a bit awkward to draw without it looking like a bunch of ballet dancing spiders — just make sure each central carbon is connected to four others.

   c) Diamond has electrons in localised covalent bonds [1 mark], so is a poor electrical conductor [1 mark]. Graphite has delocalised electrons between the sheets [1 mark] which can flow, so is a good electrical conductor [1 mark].

2)

   [2 marks for reasonable diagram showing closely packed Cu^{2+} ions and a sea of delocalised electrons]
   Metallic bonding results from the attraction between positive metal ions [1 mark] and a sea of delocalised electrons [1 mark].

Page 33 — Shapes of Molecules

1) a) NCl_3 [1 mark] BCl_3 [1 mark]

   b) NCl_3 [1 mark]

   shape: pyramidal [1 mark],
   bond angle: 107° (accept between 105° and 109°) [1 mark]

   BCl_3 [1 mark]

   (It must be a reasonable "Y" shaped molecule.)
   shape: trigonal planar [1 mark],
   bond angle: 120° exactly [1 mark]

   c) BCl_3 has three electron pairs only around B. [1 mark]
   NCl_3 has four electron pairs around N [1 mark], including one lone pair. [1 mark]

Page 35 — Electronegativity and Intermolecular Forces

1) a) The power of an atom to withdraw electron density [1 mark] from a covalent bond [1 mark] OR the ability of an atom to attract the bonding electrons [1 mark] in a covalent bond [1 mark].

   b) (i) Br —— Br   (ii)

   (iii)

   [1 mark for correct shape, 1 mark for bond polarities on H_2O, 1 mark for bond polarities on NH_3.]

2) a) Van der Waals OR instantaneous/temporary dipole-induced dipole OR dispersion forces.
   Permanent dipole-dipole interactions/forces.
   Hydrogen bonding.
   (Permanent dipole-induced dipole interactions.)
   [1 mark each for any three]

   b) (i) More energy [1 mark] is needed to break the hydrogen bonds between water molecules [1 mark].

   (ii)

   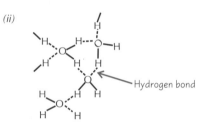

   Hydrogen bond

   Your diagram should show the following —
   • Labelled hydrogen bonds between the water molecules [1 mark].
   • At least two hydrogen bonds between an oxygen atom and a hydrogen atom on adjacent molecules [1 mark].

Page 37 — Van der Waals Forces

1) a) A — Ionic   B — (Simple) molecular
   C — Metallic   D — Giant molecular (macromolecular)
   [1 mark for each]

   b) (i) Diamond — D   (ii) Aluminium — C
   (iii) Sodium chloride — A (iv) Iodine — B
   [2 marks for all four correct. 1 mark for two correct.]

2) **Magnesium** has a metallic crystal lattice (it has metallic bonding) [1 mark]. It has a sea of electrons/delocalised electrons/freely moving electrons [1 mark], which allow it to conduct electricity in the solid or liquid state [1 mark].
   Sodium chloride has a (giant) ionic lattice [1 mark]. It doesn't conduct electricity when it's solid [1 mark] because its ions don't move freely, but vibrate about a fixed point [1 mark]. Sodium chloride conducts electricity when liquid/molten [1 mark] or in aqueous solution [1 mark] because it has freely moving ions (not electrons) [1 mark].
   Graphite is giant covalent/macromolecular [1 mark]. It has delocalised/freely moving electrons [1 mark] within the layers. It conducts electricity along the layers in the solid state [1 mark].

Answers

Unit 1: Section 3 — The Periodic Table

Page 39 — The Periodic Table
1) a) Sodium $1s^2 2s^2 2p^6 3s^1$ [1 mark]
  b) s block [1 mark]
  c) Bromine $1s^2 2s^2 2p^6 3s^2 3p^6 3d^{10} 4s^2 4p^5$ [1 mark]
  d) p block [1 mark]

Page 41 — Periodic Trends
1) Increasing number of protons means a stronger pull from the positively charged nucleus [1 mark] making it harder to remove an electron from the outer shell [1 mark]. There are no extra inner electrons to add to the shielding effect [1 mark].
2) Mg has more delocalised electrons per atom [1 mark] and the ion has a greater charge density [1 mark]. This gives Mg a stronger metal-metal bond, resulting in a higher boiling point [1 mark].
3) a) Si has a giant covalent lattice structure [1 mark] consisting of very strong covalent bonds [1 mark].
  b) Sulfur (S_8) has a larger molecule than phosphorus (P_4) [1 mark]. which results in larger van der Waals forces of attraction between molecules [1 mark].
4) The atomic radius decreases across the period from left to right [1 mark]. The number of protons increases, so nuclear charge increases [1 mark], meaning electrons are pulled closer to the nucleus [1 mark]. The electrons are all added to the same outer shell, so there's little effect on shielding [1 mark].

Page 43 — Group 2 — The Alkaline Earth Metals
1) First ionisation energy of Ca is smaller [1 mark] because Ca has (one) more electron shell(s) [1 mark]. This reduces the attraction between the nucleus and the outer electrons OR increases shielding effect [1 mark]. The outer shell of Ca is also further from the nucleus [1 mark].
2) a) $2Ca_{(s)} + O_{2(g)} \rightarrow 2CaO_{(s)}$ [1 mark]
  b) From 0 to +2 [1 mark]
  c) White [1 mark] solid [1 mark]
  d) Ionic [1 mark]
  ...because as everybody who's anybody knows, Group 2 compounds (including oxides) are generally white ionic solids.
3) a) Y [1 mark]
  b) Y has the largest radius [1 mark] so it will be furthest down the group / have the smallest ionisation energy [1 mark].

Page 45 — Group 7 — The Halogens
1) a) $I_2 + 2At^- \rightarrow 2I^- + At_2$ [1 mark]
  b) The (sodium) astatide [1 mark]
2) Aqueous solutions of both halides are tested [1 mark]. First, some dilute nitric acid is added [1 mark].
  Sodium chloride — silver nitrate gives white precipitate which dissolves in dilute ammonia solution [1 mark].
  $Ag^+ + Cl^- \rightarrow AgCl$ [1 mark]
  Sodium bromide — silver nitrate gives cream precipitate which is only soluble in concentrated ammonia solution [1 mark].
  $Ag^+ + Br^- \rightarrow AgBr$ [1 mark]
3) a) The melting and boiling points of the halogens increase down the group [1 mark]. Iodine is a solid at r.t.p. [1 mark], so you would expect that astatine is also a solid at r.t.p. [1 mark].
  b) AgI is insoluble in concentrated ammonia solution [1 mark]. The solubility of halides in ammonia solution decreases down the group [1 mark], so you would expect AgAt **NOT** to dissolve either [1 mark].
  Question 2 is the kind of question that could completely throw you if you're not really clued up on the facts. If you really know p45, then in part b) you'll go, "Ah - ha!!! Solubility of silver halides in ammonia decreases down the group..." If not, you basically won't have a clue. The moral is... it really is just about learning all the facts. Boring, but true.

Page 47 — Disproportionation and Water Treatment
1) a) $2OH^- + Cl_2 \rightarrow OCl^- + Cl^- + H_2O$ [1 mark]
  Disproportionation is simultaneous oxidation and reduction of an element in a reaction [1 mark]. Cl_2 has been reduced to Cl^- [1 mark] and oxidised to OCl^- [1 mark].
  b) E.g. water treatment, bleaching paper, bleaching textiles, cleaning [1 mark for each of two sensible applications.]
2) a) $2I^- + ClO^- + H_2O \rightarrow I_2 + Cl^- + 2OH^-$
  [2 marks — 1 for correct formulas, 1 for balancing the equation.]
  b) Iodine: −1 to 0 — oxidation   [1 mark]
  Chlorine: +1 to −1 — reduction   [1 mark]
  c) Violet/pink [1 mark]
  The colour formed would be due to the iodine.

Unit 2: Section 1 — Basic Concepts and Hydrocarbons

Page 49 — Basic Stuff
1) a)

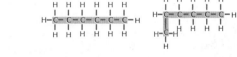

butan-1-ol   1-bromobutane
  [1 mark for each correct structure]
  b) −OH (hydroxyl) [1 mark].
  It could be attached to the first or second carbon OR butan-2-ol also exists OR because the position of the −OH group affects its chemistry [1 mark].
2) A = pentane [1 mark]
  B = methylbutane [1 mark for methyl, 1 mark for butane]
  There's only actually one type of methylbutane. You can't have 1-methylbutane — it'd be exactly the same as pentane.
  C = 2,2-dimethylpropane
  [1 mark for 2,2-, 1 mark methyl, 1 mark for propane]

Page 51 — Isomerism
1) a) (i)

hexane   2–methylpentane   2,3–dimethylbutane

3–methylpentane   2,2–dimethylbutane

  [1 mark for each correctly drawn isomer,
  1 mark for each correct name]
  (ii) The same molecular formula [1 mark] but different arrangements of the carbon skeleton [1 mark].
  Watch out — the atoms can rotate around the single C–C bonds, so these two aren't isomers — they're just the same molecule bent a bit.

  b) (i)

Z-1-chloropropene   E-1-chloropropene
[or cis-1-chloropropene]   [or trans-1-chloropropene]

  [1 mark for each correctly drawn isomer,
  1 mark for each correct name]

Answers

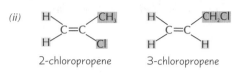

(ii)

2-chloropropene   3-chloropropene

*[1 mark for each correctly drawn isomer,
1 mark for each correct name]*

c) *A group of compounds [1 mark] that can be represented by the same general formula OR having the same functional group OR with similar chemical properties [1 mark].*

Page 53 — Atom Economy and Percentage Yield

1) a) *2 is an addition reaction [1 mark]*
   b) *For reaction 1: % atom economy*
   $= M_r(C_2H_5Cl) \div [M_r(C_2H_5Cl) + M_r(POCl_3) + M_r(HCl)]$ *[1 mark]*
   $= [(2 \times 12) + (5 \times 1) + 35.5]$
   $\div [(2 \times 12) + (5 \times 1) + 35.5$
   $+ 31 + 16 + (3 \times 35.5) + 1 + 35.5] \times 100\%$ *[1 mark]*
   $= (64.5 \div 254.5) \times 100\% = 25.3\%$ *[1 mark]*
   c) *The atom economy is 100% because there is only one product (there are no by-products) [1 mark]*
2) a) *There is only one product, so the theoretical yield can be calculated by adding the masses of the reactants [1 mark].
   So theoretical yield = 0.275 + 0.142 = 0.417 g [1 mark]*
   b) *percentage yield = (0.198 ÷ 0.417) × 100 = 47.5% [1 mark]*
   c) *Changing reaction conditions will have no effect on atom economy [1 mark]. Since the equation shows that there is only one product, the atom economy will always be 100% [1 mark].*
   Atom economy is related to the type of reaction — addition, substitution, etc. — not to the quantities of products and reactants.

Page 55 — Alkanes

1) a) *One with no double bonds OR the maximum number of hydrogens OR single bonds only [1 mark]. It contains only hydrogen and carbon atoms [1 mark].*
   b) $C_2H_{6(g)} + 3\frac{1}{2}O_{2(g)} \rightarrow 2CO_{2(g)} + 3H_2O_{(g)}$
   [1 mark for correct symbols, 1 mark for balancing]
2) a) *Nonane is an alkane [1 mark].*
   b) *Nonane will have a higher boiling point than 2,2,3,3-tetramethylpentane [1 mark] because the molecules of branched-chain alkanes like 2,2,3,3-tetramethylpentane are less closely packed together than their straight-chain isomers, so they have weaker Van der Waals forces holding them together [1 mark].*
   c) (i) $C_9H_{20} + 9\frac{1}{2}O_2 \rightarrow 9CO + 10H_2O$ *[1 mark]*
   (ii) *Carbon monoxide binds to haemoglobin in the blood in preference to oxygen [1 mark], so less oxygen can be carried around the body, leading to oxygen deprivation [1 mark].*
   d) *Nonane is a larger molecule than methane, so it contains more bonds [1 mark]. The energy released is due to the breaking and then reforming of bonds [1 mark].*

Page 57 — Petroleum

1) a) (i) *There's greater demand for smaller fractions [1 mark] for motor fuels [1 mark]. Alternatively: There's greater demand for alkenes [1 mark] to make petrochemicals/polymers [1 mark].*
   (ii) *E.g. $C_{12}H_{26} \rightarrow C_2H_4 + C_{10}H_{22}$ [1 mark].*
   There are loads of possible answers — just make sure the C's and H's balance and there's an alkane and an alkene.
   b) (i) *Branched-chain alkanes, cycloalkanes, arenes [1 mark for each].*
   (ii) *They reduce knocking (autoignition) [1 mark].*
   (iii)

2-methylbutane   2, 2-dimethylpropane

[1 mark for each structure, 1 mark for each name]

Page 59 — Fossil Fuels

1) a) *Fermentation [1 mark]*
   b) *It is carbon neutral because the carbon dioxide taken in as the plant grows [1 mark] is equal to the carbon dioxide released as the fuel burns [1 mark]*
   c) *Poorer countries may try to earn money by growing suitable crops, meaning less land will be available for them to grow food [1 mark]. Clearing forests to grow crops leads to loss of biodiversity and damage to the environment [1 mark].*
2) a) *Burning them is very exothermic [1 mark].*
   b) *Burning fossil fuels releases carbon dioxide [1 mark], which is a greenhouse gas, so it enhances the greenhouse effect [1 mark].*
   c) *Fossil fuels take millions of years to form [1 mark], so once they have been used, they cannot be replaced [1 mark].*
   d) *They are the raw material for many organic chemicals [1 mark].*

Page 61 — Alkanes — Substitution Reactions

1) a) *Free radical substitution. [1 mark]*
   b) $CH_4 + Br_2 \xrightarrow{U.V\ light} CH_3Br + HBr$ *[1 mark[*
   c) $Br\cdot + CH_4 \rightarrow HBr + CH_3\cdot$ *[1 mark]*
   $CH_3\cdot + Br_2 \rightarrow CH_3Br + Br\cdot$ *[1 mark]*
   d) (i) *Two methyl radicals bond together to form an ethane molecule. [1 mark]*
   (ii) *Termination step [1 mark]*
   (iii) $CH_3\cdot + CH_3\cdot \rightarrow CH_3CH_3$ *[1 mark]*
   e) *Tetrabromomethane [1 mark]*
2) $CH_3CH_3 + Br_2 \xrightarrow{U.V\ light} CH_3CH_2Br + HBr$ *[1 mark]*
   Initiation: $Br_2 \xrightarrow{U.V\ light} 2Br\cdot$ *[1 mark]*
   Propagation: $CH_3CH_3 + Br\cdot \rightarrow CH_3CH_2\cdot + HBr$ *[1 mark]*
        $CH_3CH_2\cdot + Br_2 \rightarrow CH_3CH_2Br + Br\cdot$ *[1 mark]*
   Termination: $CH_3CH_2\cdot + Br\cdot \rightarrow CH_3CH_2Br$ *[1 mark]*
   Or: $CH_3CH_2\cdot + CH_3CH_2\cdot \rightarrow CH_3CH_2CH_2CH_3$ *[1 mark]*
   [1 mark for mentioning U.V.]
   Watch out — you're asked for the reaction with ethane here.
   It's just the same as the methane reaction though.

Page 63 — Alkenes and Polymers

1) a) *The carbon atoms in ethene are joined by a double bond [1 mark], consisting of:
   A sigma (σ) bond between the s-orbitals of the carbon atoms*

    [1 mark]

   A pi (π) bond between the p-orbitals *[1 mark]*

   b) *Ethene is a planar molecule [1 mark]. The atoms cannot move around the C=C double bond [1 mark] because the π bond does not allow rotation [1 mark].*
   c) *Ethene is useful because it is very reactive [1 mark] and is the starting point for making many different polymers [1 mark].*

   d)

   (you can also put $CH_2=CH_2$)

   [1 mark]

   [1 mark]

Answers

Page 65 — Polymers and the Environment

1) a) Saves on landfill
OR Energy can be used to generate electricity [1 mark for either]
b) Toxic gases produced [1 mark].
Scrubbers can be used [1 mark] to remove these toxic gases.
2) Melted [1 mark] and remoulded [1 mark]
OR Cracked [1 mark] and processed [1 mark] to make a new object.
3) Renewable raw material / Less energy used (in manufacture) /
Less CO_2 produced over lifetime of polymer (if used to replace
plastics that are usually burnt)
[1 mark for each, up to a maximum of 2 marks]

Page 67 — Reactions of Alkenes

1) a) Shake the alkene with bromine water [1 mark], and the
solution goes colourless if a double bond is present [1 mark].
b) Electrophilic [1 mark] addition [1 mark].
c)

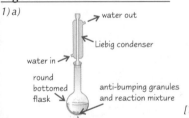

[1 mark]   [1 mark]

Unit 2: Section 2 — Alcohols, Halogenoalkanes and Analysis

Page 69 — Alcohols

1) a) Butan-1-ol [1 mark], primary [1 mark]
b) 2-methylpropan-2-ol [1 mark], tertiary [1 mark]
c) Butan-2-ol [1 mark], secondary [1 mark]
d) 2-methylpropan-1-ol [1 mark], primary [1 mark]
2) a) Primary [1 mark]. The -OH group is bonded to a carbon with one
alkyl group/other carbon atom attached [1 mark].
b) (i) $C_6H_{12}O_{6(aq)} \rightarrow 2C_2H_5OH_{(aq)} + 2CO_{2(g)}$ [1 mark]
(ii) Temperature between 30 and 40 °C [1 mark],
Anaerobic conditions OR air/oxygen excluded [1 mark]
(Allow 'yeast' as an alternative to one of the above.)
c) Ethene is cheap and abundantly available / It's a low-cost process /
it's a high-yield process / Very pure ethanol is produced / Fast
reaction [1 mark each for up to two of these reasons]. This might
change in the future as crude oil reserves run out or become more
expensive [1 mark].

Page 71 — Oxidation of Alcohols

1) a)

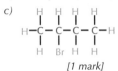

water out
Liebig condenser
water in
round bottomed flask
anti-bumping granules and reaction mixture
heat
[1 mark for diagram]

You set up reflux apparatus in this way so that the reaction can be
heated to boiling point [1 mark] without losing any materials/
reactants/products OR so vapour will condense and drip back into
the flask [1 mark]

b) (i) Propanoic acid [1 mark]
(ii) $CH_3CH_2CH_2OH + [O] \rightarrow CH_3CH_2CHO + H_2O$ [1 mark]
$CH_3CH_2CHO + [O] \rightarrow CH_3CH_2COOH$ [1 mark]
(iii) Distillation [1 mark]. This is so aldehyde is removed immediately
as it forms [1 mark].
If you don't get the aldehyde out quick-smart, it'll be a carboxylic acid
before you know it.

c) (i)

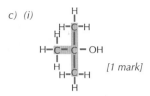

[1 mark]

(ii) 2-methylpropan-2-ol is a tertiary alcohol (which is more stable)
[1 mark].

Page 74 — Halogenoalkanes

1) a) Chlorofluorocarbons (CFCs) [1 mark]
b) [1 mark each for any three of the following]
non-toxic, non-flammable, stable, volatile
2 a)

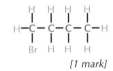

[1 mark]

b)

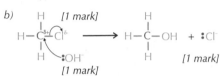

[1 mark]

[1 mark]

c) A white [1 mark] precipitate [1 mark]
d) Iodomethane would be hydrolysed more quickly than chloromethane
[1 mark].

Page 77 — Analytical Techniques

1 a) A's due to an O–H group in a carboxylic acid [1 mark].
B's due to a C=O as in an aldehyde, ketone, acid or ester [1 mark].
b) The spectrum suggests it's a carboxylic acid — it's got a COOH group
[1 mark]. This group has a mass of 45, so the rest of the molecule has
a mass of 29 (74 – 45), which is likely to be C_2H_5 [1 mark]. So the
molecule could be C_2H_5COOH — propanoic acid [1 mark].
2) a) 44 [1 mark]
b) X has a mass of 15. It is probably an methyl group/CH_3. [1 mark]
Y has a mass of 29. It is probably an ethyl group/C_2H_5. [1 mark]
c)

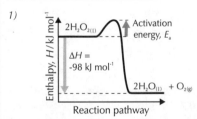

[1 mark]

d) If the compound was an alcohol, you would expect a peak with m/z
ratio of 17 [1 mark], caused by the OH fragment [1 mark].

Unit 2: Section 3 — Energy

Page 79 — Enthalpy Changes

1)

Enthalpy, H / kJ mol^{-1}
$2H_2O_{2(l)}$
Activation energy, E_a
$\Delta H = -98$ kJ mol^{-1}
$2H_2O_{(l)} + O_{2(g)}$
Reaction pathway

Reactants lower in energy than products [1 mark]. Activation energy
correctly labelled [1 mark]. ΔH correctly labelled with arrow pointing
downwards [1 mark].
For an exothermic reaction, the ΔH arrow points downwards, but for an
endothermic reaction it points upwards. The activation energy arrow
always points upwards though.

Answers

2) a) $CH_3OH_{(l)} + 1\frac{1}{2}O_{2(g)} \rightarrow CO_{2(g)} + 2H_2O_{(l)}$
Correct balanced equation [1 mark]. Correct state symbols [1 mark].
It is perfectly OK to use halves to balance equations. Make sure that only 1 mole of CH_3OH is combusted, as it says in the definition for $\Delta H_c^\ominus$.

b) $C_{(s)} + 2H_{2(g)} + \frac{1}{2}O_{2(g)} \rightarrow CH_3OH_{(l)}$
Correct balanced equation [1 mark]. Correct state symbols [1 mark].

c) H_2O should be formed under standard conditions (i.e. liquid, not gas) [1 mark]. Only 1 mole of C_3H_8 should be shown according to the definition of $\Delta H_c^\ominus$ [1 mark].
You really need to know the definitions of the standard enthalpy changes off by heart. There are loads of nit-picky little details they could ask you questions about.

3) a) $C_{(s)} + O_{2\ (g)} \rightarrow CO_{2\ (g)}$
[1 mark for correct equation, 1 mark for correct state symbols]

b) It has the same value because it is the same reaction [1 mark].

c) 1 tonne = 1 000 000 g
1 mole of carbon is 12 g
so 1 tonne is 1 000 000 ÷ 12 = 83 333 moles [1 mark]
1 mole releases 393.5 kJ
so 1 tonne will release 83333 × 393.5 = 32 791 666 kJ [1 mark]

Page 81 — More on Enthalpy Changes

1) No. of moles of $CuSO_4 = \dfrac{0.2 \times 50}{1000} = 0.01$ moles [1 mark]
From the equation, 1 mole of $CuSO_4$ reacts with 1 mole of Zn.
So, 0.01 moles of $CuSO_4$ reacts with 0.01 moles of Zn [1 mark].
Heat produced by reaction= $mc\Delta T$
$= 50 \times 4.18 \times 2.6 = 543.4$ J [1 mark]
0.01 moles of zinc produces 543.4 J of heat, therefore 1 mole of zinc produces $\dfrac{543.4}{0.01}$ [1 mark] $= 54\ 340$ J ≈ 54.3 kJ
So the enthalpy change is **–54.3 kJ mol⁻¹** (you need the minus sign because it's exothermic) [1 mark for correct number, 1 mark for minus sign].
It'd be dead easy to work out the heat produced by the reaction, breathe a sigh of relief and sail on to the next question. But you need to find out the enthalpy change when 1 mole of zinc reacts. It's always a good idea to reread the question and check you've actually answered it.

2) a) A chemical reaction always involves bond breaking which needs energy / is endothermic [1 mark] and bond making which releases energy / is exothermic [1 mark]. Whether the reaction is exothermic or endothermic depends on whether more energy is used to break bonds or released by forming new bonds over the whole reaction [1 mark].

b) Use the formula Q= $mc\Delta T$ [1 mark]
m = 1 kg =1000 g
c = 4.18 J g⁻¹K⁻¹
6 g of carbon is 0.5 moles [1 mark]
So Q = 0.5 × 393.5 = 196.75 kJ = 196 750 J [1 mark]
So 196 750 = 1000 × 4.18 × ΔT
ΔT = 196 750 ÷ 4180 = 47.1 K [1 mark]

Page 83 — Enthalpy Calculations

1) $\Delta H_r^\ominus$ = sum of $\Delta H_f^\ominus$(products) – sum of $\Delta H_f^\ominus$(reactants)
= [0 + (3 × –602)] [1 mark] – [–1676 + (3 × 0)] [1 mark]
= **–130 kJ mol⁻¹** [1 mark]
Don't forget the units. It's a daft way to lose marks.

2) $\Delta H_r^\ominus$ = $\Delta H_c^\ominus$(glucose) – 2 × $\Delta H_c^\ominus$(ethanol) [1 mark]
= [–2820] – [(2 × –1367)] [1 mark]
= **–86 kJ mol⁻¹** [1 mark]

3) $\Delta H_f^\ominus$ = sum of $\Delta H_c^\ominus$(reactants) – $\Delta H_c^\ominus$(propane) [1 mark]
= [(3 × –394) + (4 × –286)] – [–2220] [1 mark]
= **–106 kJ mol⁻¹** [1 mark]

4) Total energy required to break bonds = (4 × 435) + (2 × 498)
= 2736 kJ [1 mark]
Energy released when bonds form = (2 × 805) + (4 × 464)
= 3466 kJ [1 mark]
Net energy change = +2736 + (–3466) = **–730 kJmol⁻¹**
[1 mark for correct numerical value, 1 mark for correct unit]

Page 85 — Reaction Rates

1) Increasing the pressure will increase the rate of reaction [1 mark] because the molecules will be closer together, so they are more likely to collide, and therefore more likely to react [1 mark].

2) a) X
The X curve shows the same total number of molecules as the 25°C curve, but more of them have lower energy.

b) The smaller area to the right of the activation energy line shows fewer molecules [1 mark] will have enough energy to react [1 mark]. / The shape of the curve shows fewer molecules [1 mark] have the required activation energy [1 mark].

Page 87 — Catalysts

1) a)

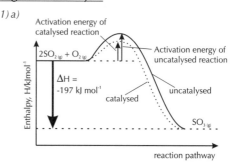

Curve showing activation energy [1 mark]. This must link reactants and products. Showing exothermic change (products **lower** in energy than reactants), with ΔH correctly labelled and a **downward** arrow [1 mark]. Correctly labelling activation energy (from reactants to highest energy peak) [1 mark].
Label your axes correctly. (No, not the sharp tools for chopping wood or heads off — you know what I mean.)

b) See the diagram above. Reaction profile showing a **greater** activation energy than for the catalysed reaction [1 mark].
Remember — catalysts lower the activation energy. So uncatalysed reactions have greater activation energies.

c) Catalysts increase the rate of the reaction by providing an alternative reaction pathway [1 mark], with a lower activation energy [1 mark].

2) a) $2H_2O_{2(l)} \rightarrow 2H_2O_{(l)} + O_{2(g)}$
Correct symbols [1 mark] and balancing equation [1 mark]. You get the marks even if you forgot the state symbols.

b)

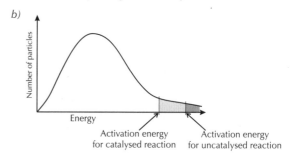

Correct general shape of the curve [1 mark]. Correctly labelling the axes [1 mark]. Activation energies marked on the horizontal axis — the catalysed activation energy must be lower than the uncatalysed activation energy [1 mark].
You don't have to draw another curve for the catalysed reaction. Just mark the lower activation energy on the one you've already done.

c) Manganese(IV) oxide lowers the activation energy by providing an alternative reaction pathway [1 mark]. So, more reactant molecules have the activation energy [1 mark], meaning there are more successful collisions in a given period of time, and so the rate increases [1 mark].

Answers

Page 89 — Dynamic Equilibrium

1) a) If a reaction at equilibrium is subjected to a change in concentration, pressure or temperature, the equilibrium will shift to try to oppose (counteract) the change. [1 mark].
Examiners are always asking for definitions so learn them — they're easy marks.

b) (i) There's no change [1 mark]. There's the same number of molecules/moles on each side of the equation [1 mark].

(ii) Reducing temperature removes heat. So the equilibrium shifts in the exothermic direction to release heat [1 mark]. The reverse reaction is exothermic (since the forward reaction is endothermic). So, the position of equilibrium shifts left [1 mark].

(iii) Removing nitrogen monoxide reduces its concentration. The equilibrium position shifts right to try and increase the nitrogen monoxide concentration again [1 mark].

c) No effect [1 mark].
Catalysts don't affect the equilibrium position.
They just help the reaction to get there sooner.

Unit 2: Section 4 — Resources

Page 91 — Green Chemistry

1) a) Ethanol is from a renewable resource (sugar cane) but petrol is from crude oil, which is non-renewable. [1 mark]
Ethanol from sugar cane can be a carbon neutral fuel. [1 mark]

b) The climate in some countries is unsuitable for growing sugar cane. [1 mark]

c) Land used for food production may be taken up growing the sugar cane, increasing the cost of food. [1 mark]
Forests may be cleared to plant sugar cane. [1 mark]

2) a) If a catalyst is used:
less energy is needed for the process [1 mark]
more efficient processes are made possible [1 mark]

b) The process has 100% atom economy as only one product is made [1 mark] so no waste is produced [1 mark].

Page 93 — The Greenhouse Effect

1) a) Water vapour [1 mark], carbon dioxide [1 mark], methane [1 mark]

b) The molecule/bond absorbs infrared radiation and the bond's vibrational energy increases. [1 mark]
Energy is transferred to other molecules by collision. [1 mark]
The average kinetic energy of the molecules increases, so the temperature increases. [1 mark]

c) How much radiation one molecule of the gas absorbs [1 mark]
How much of the gas there is in the atmosphere [1 mark]

2) a) Increased use of fossil fuels [1 mark]
Increased deforestation [1 mark]

b) Scientists have produced evidence that the Earth's average temperature has dramatically increased in recent years [1 mark].

c) Capturing CO_2 and storing it in underground rock formations/storing it deep in the ocean/converting it to stable minerals / Developing alternative fuels / Increasing photosynthesis e.g. by increasing growth of phytoplankton [1 mark each method, up to a maximum of 2 marks]

Page 96 — The Ozone Layer and Air Pollution

1) a) Ozone is formed by the effect of UV radiation from the Sun on oxygen molecules. [1 mark] The oxygen molecules split to form oxygen free radicals [1 mark] which react with more oxygen molecules to form ozone. [1 mark]

b) UV radiation can cause skin cancer. [1 mark] The ozone layer prevents most harmful UV radiation from the Sun from reaching the Earth's surface. [1 mark]

c) The ozone molecules interact with UV radiation to form an oxygen molecule and a free oxygen radical [1 mark]
$O_3 + hv \rightarrow O_2 + O\bullet$ [1 mark]
The radical produced then forms more ozone with an O_2 molecule.
$O_2 + O\bullet \rightarrow O_3$ [1 mark]

2) a) $N_{2(g)} + O_{2(g)} \rightarrow 2NO_{(g)}$ [1 mark for correct reactants and products, 1 mark for correct balancing]

b) $2NO_{(g)} + O_{2(g)} \rightarrow 2NO_{2(g)}$ [1 mark for correct reactants and products, 1 mark for correct balancing]

c) Acid rain OR smog [1 mark]

Index

Index

Index